THE
# Optimal Design
OF
# Chemical Reactors

A STUDY IN DYNAMIC PROGRAMMING

# MATHEMATICS IN
# SCIENCE AND ENGINEERING

### A Series of Monographs and Textbooks

*Edited by*

### Richard Bellman

*The RAND Corporation, Santa Monica, California*

# THE
# *Optimal Design*
## OF
# *Chemical Reactors*
## A STUDY IN DYNAMIC PROGRAMMING

RUTHERFORD ARIS

*Department of Chemical Engineering*
*Institute of Technology*
*University of Minnesota*
*Minneapolis, Minnesota*

1961

New York     *ACADEMIC PRESS*     London

ACADEMIC PRESS INC.
111 Fifth Avenue
New York 3. N. Y.

*United Kingdom Edition*
Published by
ACADEMIC PRESS INC. (London) Ltd.
17 Old Queen Street, London S.W. 1

*Library of Congress Catalog Card Number 61-14137*

PRINTED IN THE UNITED STATES OF AMERICA

# TO MY WIFE

*Uxor vivamus ut viximus et teneamus*
*nomina quae primo sumpsimus in thalamo;*
*nec ferat ulla dies, ut commutemur in aevo,*
*quin tibi sim iuvenis tuque puella mihi.*

# Preface

This monograph, as its subtitle indicates, treats some of the significant problems of chemical reactor engineering from a unified point of view. The methods of dynamic programming have proved themselves both powerful and versatile in a number of branches of economics and engineering and it is remarkable how naturally they fit the needs of reactor design. The chemical engineer will be interested in the method as a practical tool in the design process, and it is hoped that he will find here a sufficient variety of example to allow him to treat any specific problem with as much realism as he may desire. In the interest of clarity the simpler problems have been chosen for extended treatment, but in all cases the methods of solution of the more general have been shown. Mathematicians and those interested in the rapidly developing field of mathematical programming will find here an ecological study of the species whose anatomy, physiology, and natural history have been opened up in Bellman's book.

Even in the writing of so slight a work as this an author incurs debts of gratitude almost too numerous to discharge. My interest in the design of chemical reactors was first aroused by work done in the employ of Imperial Chemical Industries under the direction of Dr. B. W. Bradford and Dr. N. Levy. My understanding of the basic problems was greatly helped by discussions with the (then) Misses D. Annable and M. Jones (now respectively Mrs. Rochester and Mrs. Vincent), and particularly by Dr. F. F. Snowden who clamored for an optimum when as yet I had no idea how to give him one. To Professor N. R. Amundson I owe thanks both for the original suggestion that dynamic programming would illuminate these problems and also for many a kindness that has eased my research and writing. I have also greatly benefited from the kind interest of Professor K. G. Denbigh, whose pioneer work first drew attention to the importance of optimal design. No one who has had any contact with Dr. R. Bellman, the "fons et origo" of dynamic programming, will be ignorant of the vitality and inspiration of his mathematical ideas. His interest and that of his Rand colleague Dr. R. Kalaba in this field of application has been a great stimulus to my work. My students Messrs. Anshus, Lee, Rudd, Westbrook, and Yesberg, have helped me in several examples and calculations, Mr. Blakemore has assisted with the proofreading and Mr. Lee with the making of the index. I would like also to thank Mr. John Grund for the excellence of his draftsmanship and his patience in dealing with my frequent changes in the figures.

A first draft of Chapters 1–7 formed the substance of a thesis for which a Ph.D. in the Faculty of Science was awarded by the University of London. I am also greatly obliged to the Graduate School of the University of Minnesota for a Summer Research Fellowship that has allowed me to complete the writing of this monograph.

To my sister-in-law, Mrs. P. Blair, I owe a special debt of thanks for translating my meandering manuscript into a faultless typescript. My obligations to my wife are too personal to be detailed but too real to be overlooked.

What I owe to the works of Ausonius and the Reverend Charles Lutwidge Dodgson will be manifest to all.

RUTHERFORD ARIS

*Department of Chemical Engineering,*
*University of Minnesota*
*February 1961*

# Contents

## Chapter 1. Introduction                                    1

## Chapter 2. The Principal Notions of
## Dynamic Programming                               13

## Chapter 3. Mathematical Models for Reactor Design   31

## Chapter 4. The Objective Function     55

## Chapter 5. The Continuous Flow Stirred Tank Reactor     63

## Chapter 6. The Multibed Adiabatic Reactor     105

# 1       Introduction

*'Just the place for a Snark!' the Bellman cried,*
   *As he landed his crew with care;*
*Supporting each man on the top of the tide*
   *By a finger entwined in his hair.*

It IS MANY YEARS since a realization of the finiteness of natural resources and the pressure of business competition forced the chemical industry to begin seeking greater and greater efficiency. In this search the ingenuity and inventiveness of the practical man have held a strong lead over the analysis of the theoretician. However, a greater understanding of the underlying processes has gradually allowed them to be formulated in mathematical terms and made way for design calculations of increasing range and accuracy. At the same time the development of high speed computing machinery has made possible calculations that a few years ago would have taken prohibitively long. The skill and experience of practical operation are still of the first importance, and theoretical analysis, rather than herald itself as the leader of a new age, does well to offer its services in a more humble spirit, not as queen but as a handmaid.

Nevertheless, analysis has services to offer that must not be overlooked if the progress of the last few years is to be maintained. As in other branches of engineering, the pace of development demands that wherever possible calculation should take the place of experimentation in the endeavor to shorten the road between the decision to make a certain chemical and its final production. Indeed, there are several stages along this road where the feasibility of the whole

1

process may need to be reviewed, and at each an estimate of the optimal as well as of the practically attainable is required. Of the different outlooks on this approach Horn has written rather well. "Diejenigen, die sich selbst die 'Praktiker' nennen, blicken meist skeptisch auf die Bemühungen derjenigen, die sie als 'Theoretiker' bezeichnen. Umgekehrt neigen manche dieser 'Theoretiker' dazu, die Gültigkeit der Ergebnisse, die sie errechnet haben, zu über-schätzen, weil sie sich der Grenzen für diese Gültigkeit nicht richtig bewusst sind." We shall have occasion from time to time to observe these boundaries of validity, and will try to allay this scepticism by using mathematical notions that are essentially elementary.

The practical advantages of optimal design have been appreciated for centuries,* while the notion of an optimum has had a considerable aesthetic appeal for mathematicians. The infinitesimal calculus, the calculus of variations, and functional analysis all have something to say about the search for an extremum and all have been applied to a host of extremal problems, including those of chemical engineering. However, many of these classical methods become less suitable as the number of independent variables increases and when restrictions in the form of inequalities obtain, and to some extent the rise of the computer has diverted attention to techniques of direct calculation and away from analytical artifice. What is needed is a principle that will break down a problem with a large number of variables into manageable portions and a method which takes advantage of the speed of modern computers while still leaving room for ingenious adaptation to the features peculiar to any problem. This is provided by dynamic programming. Its methods have grown from the work of Bellman and have been given a lucid exposition in his book "Dynamic Programming" (1957). Much of the early work was stim-ulated by problems of economics and may be applied to management decisions in the chemical industry. However, the field of chemical reactor design proves to be "just the place" to find problems amena-ble to dynamic programming. They arise in an appropriate form and, in contrast with economic models, the basic soundness of the mathe-matical models is not questioned.

---

* Indeed, this appreciation goes back into legend, for Dido is credited with solving an optimal problem when having bargained for land, "taurino quantum possent circumdare tergo," she enclosed the greatest possible area with the hide cut into a fine strip. Truly, "dux femina facti"! (Aeneid, I, 364–8).

In this chapter we shall describe the principle of optimality in its general bearing on chemical processes, give a review of cognate work, and sketch its outline.

## 1.1. The Principle of Optimality

The chemical factory consists of a large number of interconnected process units, each of which is a stage in the transformation of the raw materials into finished products. It is generally desirable to make the profit resulting from this transformation as large as possible. In its widest sense this profit possesses features that can scarcely be fitted into mathematical formulas, for considerations of safety and good relations between management and labor are in the long run as important as making money. Mathematical necessity, rather than political predisposition, forces us to take a somewhat narrow view of profit and include only those elements that can be expressed in terms of monetary values and costs. Even this problem, whose solution would be of the highest value to a sufficiently enlightened management, is of too grandiose a scale to be solved at present, and we must confine our attention to units smaller than the whole factory. Some work has indeed been done on the simulation of a complete refinery within a digital computer and the use of this simulation to check and direct informed guesswork towards an optimum, but no rigorous optimization is yet possible.

As an example of a smaller unit consider a stream of reactants passing from a mixer to a preheater, then to a reactor, and on to a cooler and an extraction column. At each stage there are operating variables, as for example the temperature of the preheater or holding time of the reactor, and we are looking for an operating policy which is in some sense optimal. The process stream itself is characterized by certain state variables, such as temperature and composition, and these are transformed at each stage in a way that depends on the operating policy. The incoming stream and outgoing products have certain values, while a definite cost is involved in the choice of given operating conditions. The profit we wish to maximize is the difference between the increase in value of the stream due to the process and the cost of operation.

The approach of dynamic programming is to look first at the last stage of the process. The underlying idea is that the state of the

3

stream has been transformed at every stage of the process, but, whatever the operating policy up to the last stage, the complete policy will not be optimal unless the last stage is operating with optimal policy with respect to its feed. Thus, the first step is to determine for any possible feed state the operating policy that maximizes the profit from this stage. In our example we would consider first the operation of the extraction unit and for a range of possible feed states determine the design that will maximize the increase in value of the stream minus the operating cost of this one stage.

Next consider the last two stages of the process. There will be a combined optimal operating policy for these stages, which, for any given feed state to the first of them, will maximize the net profit from them both. In this optimal two-stage policy the first stage will not necessarily operate at the optimal one-stage policy with respect to its feed but the second stage must use the optimal policy with respect to the state of the feed that it receives from the first, for otherwise the combined policy could not possibly be optimal. Thus the maximum profit from two stages is given by:

$$
\begin{bmatrix} \text{Maximum} \\ \text{profit} \\ \text{from} \\ \text{two} \\ \text{stages} \end{bmatrix} = \underset{\text{of}}{\text{Maximum}} \begin{bmatrix} \begin{pmatrix} \text{Profit} \\ \text{from} \\ \text{first} \\ \text{stage} \end{pmatrix} + \begin{pmatrix} \text{Maximum} \\ \text{profit} \\ \text{from} \\ \text{second} \\ \text{stage} \\ \text{with} \\ \text{feed} \\ \text{produced} \\ \text{by the} \\ \text{first} \\ \text{stage} \end{pmatrix} \end{bmatrix} \quad (1)
$$

To find this maximum we have only to vary the operating conditions in the first of the two stages, since we already know the optimal operating conditions for the second. In our example the operation of the cooler is to be varied until Eq. (1) gives the greatest combined profit. This must be done for a sufficient range of possible feed states, which are the product states from the reactor.

We next consider the last three stages as two pseudo-stages, the reactor and the combined cooler and extraction unit. Since the latter has been studied and its optimal behavior is fully known we can

4

apply Eq. (1) to these pseudo-stages, for certainly the greatest profit from all three stages will not be obtained unless the cooler and extraction unit are using their combined optimal policy with respect to the output of the reactor. In this maximization we have only to vary the design of the reactor.

Proceeding in this way we build up the complete optimal policy stage by stage. At the expense of having to consider a range of possible feed states for each stage, we need only vary the operating conditions in one stage at a time. This introduces a vast economy and organization into the search for optimal conditions; otherwise, the simultaneous variation of a large number of conditions is a most frustrating business. An example given in Section 2.1 will show how the crude enumeration of alternatives can quickly lead to problems far beyond the capacity of the biggest computers.

Such is the general application of the principle of optimality to multistage processes. Clearly it has applications in many branches of chemical engineering,* but only those that concern the design of chemical reactors will engage our attention here. Much of the interest and most of the instruction in any study lies in its particular examples, and we shall give many of these in addition to outlining the general algorithms for the solution of optimal design problems.

## 1.2. Review of Cognate Work

It will be useful to have before us a brief review of what has already been published on the optimal design of chemical reactors. Fortunately this literature is not voluminous in spite of the popularity of optimization studies; for popularity produces a plethora of publications with perhaps more platitude than pith. There is indeed a considerable literature that has grown up in the general area of chemical engineering, but little of it has been cultivated in the rather narrow field that we propose to till. It may be also that much work has been done privately within the industry and has never been published. A general background to the economics of chemical processes is provided by Happel's book (1958), in which also there are some general references to optimization. A general review of the mathematics of optimization as applied to chemical engineering

* For other applications see Kalaba (1960), Aris, Rudd, and Amundson (1960), and Bellman, Kalaba, and Aris (1960).

problems was given by Amundson in his Institute Lecture to the American Institute of Chemical Engineers in 1958.

The scope of the literature with specific bearing on chemical reactor design can be best summarized as in Table 1.1 where the work

TABLE 1.1

| Type of reactor | Single reaction | Simultaneous reactions |
|---|---|---|
| Stirred tank sequence | Denbigh (1944, 1960) Horn (1958a) Piret and Trambouze (1959) | Denbigh (1944, 1951, 1958) Horn (1958a, 1961) Grütter and Messikommer (1960) Westbrook and Aris (1961) |
| Multibed adiabatic | Leitenberger (1939) Calderbank (1953) Horn (1958a) Horn and Küchler (1959) | |
| Tubular or batch | Leitenberger (1939) Denbigh (1944, 1951, 1960) Annable (1952) Calderbank (1953) Amundson (1955) Amundson and Bilous (1956) Horn (1958a, 1960) Piret and Trambouze (1959) Bellman, Kalaba, and Aris (1960) | Denbigh (1951) Amundson (1955) Amundson and Bilous (1956) Horn (1958a,b, 1960, 1961) Horn and Küchler (1959) Horn and Troltenier (1960) Katz (1960a,b) |

is classified according to the type of reactor that receives consideration. Since the complexity of the problem increases greatly when more than one reaction takes place, it is not surprising that the case of a single reaction has dominated most of the earlier work. If names may be singled out it can be said that the work of Leitenberger, Denbigh, and Amundson gives the first basic results in the general area, while by far the most extensive body of results is to be found in the work of Horn. With the exception of Grütter and Messikommer's, none of these papers has used the notions of dynamic programming, and it is interesting to see how these other methods tie in with our own.

Leitenberger's work (1939) is concerned with the oxidation of sulfur dioxide in adiabatic beds and tubular reactors. Using the Boresskow-Slinko kinetic equation he calculated the optimal temperature for any degree of conversion. For the adiabatic bed he introduced a diagram somewhat similar to Fig. 8.1, but worked with a graph of temperature and holding time in which he could make a rapid calculation of a multibed reactor with beds all working at conditions close to the maximum reaction velocity. Calderbank (1953) discussed the same reaction using a different kinetic expression. He gave an example showing that a two-bed adiabatic reactor producing 50 tons of sulfuric acid a day requires 14.7 tons of catalyst. By contrast, an optimal temperature gradient in a tubular reactor would only require 0.93 tons. The quoted figure of 4.4 tons for a commercial plant shows both that good efficiency is attained and that there is still room for improvement. Annable (1952), Leitenberger, and Calderbank, all compared the optimum temperature profile with that which actually obtains in a countercurrent-cooled tubular reactor.

Denbigh's basic work (1944) was the consideration of reaction velocity and yield in stirred tank and batch or tubular reactors. For a given conversion he showed that the stirred tank requires a much greater volume than the tubular reactor because of the lower reaction rate that prevails in the presence of complete mixing. However, he gave an example in which the volume requirements for a certain reaction are reduced tenfold by the use of two tanks instead of one. He further showed that for orders of reaction greater than unity the volumes of the stages should increase for optimal performance. The paper concludes with a discussion of the continuous variation of a parameter, such as temperature, along the reaction path. For a single reaction it is shown that the parameter should always be adjusted to maximize the local reaction rate, and this principle is applied to the ammonia synthesis reaction. In a later paper (1951) Denbigh showed that a falling temperature gradient may be optimal for the consecutive reactions $A \rightarrow B \rightarrow C$. This is indeed true, but the immediate maximization of the local reaction rate is no longer a valid principle. This distinction between the cases of one and many reactions (which in a later chapter we describe as disjunction of policy) was made by Amundson (1955) and shown very clearly by Horn (1960).

From our viewpoint one of the most interesting of Denbigh's papers is his contribution to the First European Symposium on Chemical Reaction Engineering (Denbigh, 1958). He considered the system of four reactions $A + B \rightarrow X \rightarrow Y$, $A + B \rightarrow P$, and $X \rightarrow Q$ where Y is the desired product, X an intermediate and P and Q waste products. With suitable relative rates of reaction the yield of Y can be vastly increased by the proper choice of temperature in two stirred tank reactors. An example so elegant has naturally excited some interest, and Horn (1960) has given a full discussion of the various types of optimal profile required by this reaction system; we shall consider it extensively in Section 5.6 (see also Aris, 1960a). Denbigh's contribution to the Second European Symposium (1960) concerns the optimal choice of holding time in a sequence of stirred tanks, and he introduces there the method of "maximization of rectangles," a technique peculiarly suited to dynamic programming. It was this method that suggested the graphical construction of Section 5.4.*

The work of Amundson and Bilous (1956) was the first complete treatment of the consecutive reaction system $A \rightarrow B \rightarrow C$. If the activation energy of the first step is less than that of the second it is to be expected that a decreasing temperature gradient would favor the production of B; for in the early part of the reaction a fairly high temperature is needed to prevent an excessive holding time, whereas towards the end a much lower temperature will minimize the formation of C. Amundson and Bilous developed an equation for the optimal temperature profile which could be solved simultaneously with the mass balance equations. We shall arrive at the same equations by dynamic programming in Section 7.3. The calculus of variations approach to this problem was first given by Swinnerton-Dyer (1957) in a paper on an extremal problem; the case is also discussed in detail by Katz (1960b). Horn (1958a) has given a detailed treatment of this case and shown that the results can be expressed by elementary integrals when the ratio of activation energies is rational. Katz (1960a,b) has applied the calculus of variations to the optimal profile problem in quite a general way, deriving a set of equations which are essentially the same as those given by Horn (1958a) and here in Chapter 7. He has also considered the simultaneous variation of pressure and temperature and the controlled addition of one of the reactants.

* The author is greatly indebted to Professor Denbigh for his kindness in communicating these, and other, results before publication.

8

## 1.2. REVIEW OF COGNATE WORK

The work of Horn deserves particular attention, being marked by a balanced engineering viewpoint and nice application of mathematical technique.* It stems from his dissertation (1958a) in which he treated a whole range of optimal problems for continuous chemical processes. His first concern is to show what is the least number of basic equations and to arrive at their form for the stirred tank and tubular reactors. He then proceeds to a discussion of the demands of optimization with various examples, and formulates a general algorithm. Solutions of the optimal profile problem for first- and second-order reactions are given in closed form. These involve certain integrals which are tabulated in an appendix. For more than one independent reaction the integration of ordinary differential equations is required, but for only two reactions certain simplifications are possible (cf. Amundson and Bilous, 1956; Horn, 1960; Aris, 1960e; and below Section 7.4). The solution for parallel and consecutive reactions is given in closed form. Finally, the optimal design of a multibed adiabatic reactor is considered.

This basic work has been elaborated in a number of papers. In Horn and Küchler (1959) are given the results for the adiabatic bed and some of those for the tubular reactor. In Horn's contribution to the Second European Symposium on Chemical Reaction Engineering the tubular reactor is fully discussed. It is shown that the profiles for the single reversible reaction and the parallel reactions $A_1 \rightarrow A_2$, $A_1 \rightarrow A_3$ are mirror images of each other and hence that the latter profile depends on the length of the reactor as well as on the initial state. The paper by Horn and Troltenier (1960) contains a very full discussion of Denbigh's system in a tubular reactor with the assumption that the final isothermal section is long enough to bring the reaction to completion. The sequence of stirred tank reactors is considered in Horn's latest paper (1961), and the optimal temperatures and holding times are obtained by a scheme of computation based on the introduction of Lagrange multipliers. It is shown that the dimensionality of the problem can be reduced in certain cases by means of transformations that turn out to be precisely those that have been found effective in dynamic programming.

---

* The author regrets very much his tardiness in becoming acquainted with this work and is very grateful to Dr. Horn for his personal communications. Reference should have been made to Horn's work in my papers (1960b,c,d,e).

9

This concludes our review of the chemical engineering literature.* We shall not attempt to review that of dynamic programming which, thanks to the fecundity of the notion and labors of its author, is already enormous. All that is needed here, and much more, is to be found in Bellman's book "Dynamic Programming" (1957).

## 1.3. The Scope of the Present Monograph

We shall direct our attention to the whole range of optimal problems in chemical reactor design and endeavor to give a reasonably complete account of them by the methods of dynamic programming. This is not done in ignorance or contempt of other methods but to demonstrate that all such problems can be so treated. The underlying mathematical ideas are elementary, requiring thought rather than knowledge for their comprehension. In the next chapter we allow ourselves the luxury of a relatively abstract presentation of these notions, but after this we shall be entirely concerned with banausic realities.

In Chapter 3 the basic equations for reactions and reactors are set up; the objective function needed to define a realistic optimal problem is discussed in Chapter 4. Subsequently, it is natural to consider separately the main types of chemical reactors and their associated problems. In Chapter 8 three problems with a stochastic element in them are described. Chapter 9 concerns itself with the optimal operation of existing reactors which may be regarded as partial designs in which only some of the variables can be optimally chosen. Some recent advances in optimal control, which, however, lie outside our present considerations, are to be found in the paper by Kalman, Lapidus, and Shapiro (1959) and in that of Rudd, Aris, and Amundson (1961).

It is assumed throughout that an expression for the rate of reaction in terms of the local thermodynamic variables is available. The derivation of such expressions is no easy task (see for example Hougen and Watson, 1947) and there are some commercial reactions for which no sound kinetic expression is known. Nor is it always easy to get at those that are being used, for often a company will guard

---

* The paper by Grütter and Messikommer has been shown only in passing to the author as a preprint, and he regrets that he has not been able to give it the attention it warrants.

10

them as closely as its catalyst formulas.* The methods to be described do not in any way depend on the particular form of this expression, and in certain cases the results show how improvements can be made even when the form is unknown. To see what use can be made of the expression, however, gives a better idea of what is needed in such an expression and provides an incentive for finding it.

* Such secrecy is not always necessary and is occasionally rendered ludicrous by the lengths to which it is carried. Preckshot (*Chem. Eng. Progr.*, **56**, 26, March 1960) has made some very sensible suggestions on this subject.

# The Principal
# Notions of
# Dynamic Programming

**2**

(*"That's exactly the method," the Bellman bold
In a hasty parenthesis cried,
"That's exactly the way I have always been told
That the capture of Snarks should be tried!"*)

IN THIS CHAPTER we shall describe the principles of dynamic programming with special reference to the cases that will be needed later. It is important to lay the foundation of later applications as surely and explicitly as possible and for this reason the presentation in this chapter will be relatively abstract, with little more than a passing reference to the chemical engineering interpretation. The reader in haste to reach the applications in the later chapters may wish to read this chapter rather lightly in the first instance, returning later to establish his faith more firmly. The first, second, and fourth sections will provide a basic introduction to the ideas and notation.

## 2.1. Multistage Decision Processes and the Principle of Optimality

The function of a chemical reactor is to transform the state of a batch or stream of material into a state of greater value. This process will take place in one or more stages and the resulting product will depend on the decisions made at each stage. These decisions affect the transformation of state produced at any one stage and, since the material passes from stage to stage, the state of the final product. The set of all decisions is called the operating policy or, more simply, the policy. An optimal policy is one which in some sense gets the best out of the process as a whole by maximizing the value of the product. There are thus three components to an optimal design problem:

(1) The specification of the state of the process stream;

(2) The specification of the operating variables and the transformation they effect;

(3) The specification of the objective function of which the optimization is desired.

For a chemical process the first of these might involve the concentrations of the different chemical species, and the temperature or pressure of the stream. For the second we might have to choose the volume of reactor or amount of cooling to be supplied; the way in which the transformation of state depends on the operating variables for the main types of reactors is discussed in the next chapter. The objective function is some measure of the increase in value of the stream by processing; it is the subject of Chapter 4.

The essential characteristic of an optimal policy when the state of the stream is transformed in a sequence of stages with no feedback was first isolated by Bellman. He recognized that whatever transformation may be effected in the first stage of an $R$-stage process, the remaining stages must use an optimal $(R - 1)$-stage policy with respect to the state resulting from the first stage, if there is to be any chance of optimizing the complete process. Moreover, by systematically varying the operating conditions in the first stage and always using the optimal $(R - 1)$-stage policy for the remaining stages, we shall eventually find the optimal policy for all $R$ stages. Proceeding in this way, from one to two and from two to three stages, we may gradually build up the policy for any number. At each step of the calculation the operating variables of only one stage need be varied.

To see how important this economy is, let us suppose that there are $m$ operating variables at each stage and that the state is specified by $n$ variables; then the search for the maximum at any one stage will require a number of operations of order $a^m$ (where $a$ is some number not unreasonably large). To proceed from one stage to the next a sufficient number of feed states must be investigated to allow

14

of interpolation; this number will be of the order of $b^n$. If, however, we are seeking the optimal $R$-stage policy for a given feed state, only one search for a maximum is required at the final step. Thus a number of operations of the order of $\{(R - 1)b^n + 1\}a^m$ are required. If all the operating variables were varied simultaneously, $a^{Rm}$ operations would be required to do the same job, and as $R$ increases this increases very much more rapidly than the number of operations required by the dynamic program. But even more important than this is the fact that the direct search by simultaneously varying all operating conditions has produced only one optimal policy, namely, that for the given feed state and $R$ stages. In contrast, the dynamic program produces this policy and a whole family of policies for any smaller number of stages. If the problem is enlarged to require a complete coverage of feed states, $Ra^m b^n$ operations are needed by the dynamic program and $a^{Rm} b^n$ by the direct search. But $a^{(R-1)m}$ is vastly larger than $R$. No optimism is more baseless than that which believes that the high speed of modern digital computers allows for use of the crudest of methods in searching out a result. Suppose that $m = n = 2$, $a = b = 10$, $R = 6$, and that the average operation requires only $10^{-3}$ sec. Then the dynamic program would require about a minute, whereas the direct search would take more than three millennia!

The principle of optimality thus brings a vital organization into the search for the optimal policy of a multistage decision process. Bellman (1957) has annunciated in the following terms:

"An optimal policy has the property that whatever the initial state and initial decision are, the remaining decisions must constitute an optimal policy with respect to the state resulting from the first decision."

This is the principle which we will invoke in every case to set up a functional equation. It appears in a form that is admirably suited to the powers of the digital computer. At the same time, every device that can be employed to reduce the number of variables is of the greatest value, and it is one of the attractive features of dynamic programming that room is left for ingenuity in using the special features of the problem to this end.

## 2.2. *The Discrete Deterministic Process*

Consider the process illustrated in Fig. 2.1, consisting of $R$ distinct stages. These will be numbered in the direction opposite to the flow

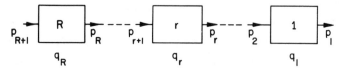

FIG. 2.1. The discrete process.

of the process stream, so that stage $r$ is the $r$th stage from the end. Let the state of the stream leaving stage $r$ be denoted by a vector $\mathbf{p}_r = (p_{1r}, p_{2r}, \ldots p_{nr})$ and the operating variables of stage $r$ by $\mathbf{q}_r = (q_{1r}, \ldots q_{mr})$. Thus $\mathbf{p}_{R+1}$ denotes the state of the feed to the $R$-stage process, and $\mathbf{p}_1$ the state of the product from the last stage. Each stage transforms the state $\mathbf{p}_{r+1}$ of its feed to the state $\mathbf{p}_r$ in a way that depends on the operating variables $\mathbf{q}_r$. We write this

$$\mathbf{p}_r = \mathfrak{I}(\mathbf{p}_{r+1};\mathbf{q}_r) = \mathfrak{I}_r(\mathbf{p}_{r+1}). \tag{1}$$

This transformation is uniquely determined by $\mathbf{q}_r$ and we therefore speak of the process as deterministic. In practical situations there will be restrictions on the admissible operating conditions, and we regard the vectors as belonging to a fixed and bounded set $S$. The set of vectors $\mathbf{q}_1, \ldots \mathbf{q}_R$ constitutes the operating policy or, more briefly, the policy, and a policy is admissible if all the $\mathbf{q}_r$ belong to $S$. When the policy has been chosen the state of the product can be obtained from the state of the feed by repeated application of the transformation (1); thus

$$\mathbf{p}_1 = \mathfrak{I}_1 \mathfrak{I}_2 \cdots \mathfrak{I}_R(\mathbf{p}_{R+1}). \tag{2}$$

The objective function, which is to be maximized, is some function, usually piecewise continuous, of the product state. Let this be denoted by

$$P(\mathbf{p}_1) = P(p_{11}, \ldots p_{n1}). \tag{3}$$

An optimal policy is an admissible policy $\mathbf{q}_1, \ldots \mathbf{q}_R$ which maximizes the objective function $P$. The policy may not be unique but the maximum value of $P$ certainly is, and once the policy is specified this maximum can be calculated by (2) and (3) as a function of the feed state $\mathbf{p}_{R+1}$. Let

$$f_R(\mathbf{p}_{R+1}) = \text{Max } P(\mathbf{p}_1) \tag{4}$$

where the maximization is over all admissible policies $\mathbf{q}_1, \ldots \mathbf{q}_R$. When it is necessary to be specific we say that the optimal policy is an optimal $R$-stage policy with respect to the feed state $\mathbf{p}_{R+1}$.

For any choice of admissible policy $\mathbf{q}_R$ in the first stage, the state of the stream leaving this stage is given by

$$\mathbf{p}_R = \Im(\mathbf{p}_{R+1}; \mathbf{q}_R). \tag{5}$$

This is the feed state of the subsequent $(R - 1)$ stages which, according to the principle of optimality, must use an optimal $(R - 1)$-stage policy with respect to this state. This will result in a value $f_{R-1}(\mathbf{p}_R)$ of the objective function, and when $\mathbf{q}_R$ is chosen correctly this will give $f_R(\mathbf{p}_{R+1})$, the maximum of the objective function. Thus

$$f_R(\mathbf{p}_{R+1}) = \text{Max } f_{R-1}(\mathbf{p}_R) \tag{6}$$

where the maximization is over all admissible policies $\mathbf{q}_R$, and $\mathbf{p}_R$ is related to $\mathbf{p}_{R+1}$ by (5). The sequence of equations (6) can be solved for $R = 2, 3 \ldots$ when $f_1$ is known, and clearly

$$f_1(\mathbf{p}_2) = \text{Max } P(\mathbf{p}_1), \tag{7}$$

the maximization being over all admissible $\mathbf{q}_1$.

The set of equations (5), (6), and the starting equation (7) is of a recursive type well suited to programming on the digital computer. In finding the optimal $R$-stage policy from that of $(R - 1)$ stages, only the function $f_{R-1}$ is needed. When $f_R$ has been found it may be transferred into the storage location of $f_{R-1}$ and the whole calculation repeated. We also see how the results may be presented, although if $n$, the number of state variables, is large any tabulation will become cumbersome. A table or set of tables may be set out as in Table 2.1.

To extract the optimal $R$-stage policy with respect to the feed state $\mathbf{p}_{R+1}$, we enter section $R$ of this table at the state $\mathbf{p}_{R+1}$ and find immediately from the last column the maximum value of the objective function. In the third column is given the optimal policy for stage $R$, and in the fourth, the resulting state of the stream when this policy is used. Since by the principle of optimality the remaining stages use an optimal $(R - 1)$-stage policy with respect to $\mathbf{p}_R$, we may enter section $(R - 1)$ of the table at this state $\mathbf{p}_R$ and read off the optimal

17

TABLE 2.1

| Number of stage from the end | Feed state | Operating policy | Product state | Maximum objective function |
|---|---|---|---|---|
| 1 | $\mathbf{p}_2$ | $\mathbf{q}_1$ | $\mathbf{p}_1$ | $f_1(\mathbf{p}_2)$ |
| 2 | $\mathbf{p}_3$ | $\mathbf{q}_2$ | $\mathbf{p}_2$ | $f_2(\mathbf{p}_3)$ |
| . | . | . | . | . |
| . | . | . | . | . |
| . | . | . | . | . |
| $R-1$ | $\mathbf{p}_R$ | $\mathbf{q}_{R-1}$ | $\mathbf{p}_{R-1}$ | $f_{R-1}(\mathbf{p}_R)$ |
| $R$ | $\mathbf{p}_{R+1}$ | $\mathbf{q}_R$ | $\mathbf{p}_R$ | $f_R(\mathbf{p}_{R+1})$ |

policy for stage $(R - 1)$ and the resulting state $\mathbf{p}_{R-1}$. Proceeding in this way up the table we extract the complete optimal policy and, if it is desired, we can check on $f_R$ by evaluating $P(\mathbf{p}_1)$ at the last stage.

It may be that the objective function depends not only on $\mathbf{p}_1$ but also on $\mathbf{q}_1, \ldots \mathbf{q}_R$, as when the cost of the operating policy is considered. A moment's reflection shows that the above algorithm and presentation work equally well in this case. A form of objective function that we shall often have occasion to consider is

$$P(\mathbf{p}_1) = V(\mathbf{p}_1) - V(\mathbf{p}_{R+1}) - \sum_{r=1}^{R} C(\mathbf{q}_r)$$

$$= \sum_{r=1}^{R} \{V(\mathbf{p}_r) - V(\mathbf{p}_{r+1}) - C(\mathbf{q}_r)\}. \tag{8}$$

Here $V(\mathbf{p})$ represents the value of the stream in state $\mathbf{p}$ and $C(\mathbf{q})$ the cost of operating the stage with conditions $\mathbf{q}$. Hence $P$ is the increase in value of the stream minus the cost of operation, that is, the net profit. If

$$P_r = V(\mathbf{p}_r) - V(\mathbf{p}_{r+1}) - C(\mathbf{q}_r) \tag{9}$$

denotes the net profit from stage $r$ and

$$f_R(\mathbf{p}_{R+1}) = \text{Max} \sum_{1}^{R} P_r, \tag{10}$$

then the principle of optimality gives

$$f_R(\mathbf{p}_{R+1}) = \text{Max} \{P_R + f_{R-1}(\mathbf{p}_R)\}. \tag{11}$$

This sequence of equations may be started with the remark that with no process $(R = 0)$ there is no profit, i.e.,

$$f_0(\mathbf{p}_1) = 0. \tag{12}$$

## 2.3. The Discrete Stochastic Process

The process in which the outcome of any one stage is known only statistically is also of interest, although for chemical reactor design it is not as important as the deterministic process. In this case the stage $r$ operating with conditions $\mathbf{q}_r$ transforms the state of the stream from $\mathbf{p}_{r+1}$ to $\mathbf{p}_r$, but only the probability distribution of $\mathbf{p}_r$ is known. This is specified by a distribution function $dG(\mathbf{p}_{r+1},\mathbf{p}_r;\mathbf{q}_r)$ such that the probability that $\mathbf{p}_r$ lies in some region $D$ of the stage space is $\int_D dG(\mathbf{p}_{r+1},\mathbf{p}_r;\mathbf{q}_r)$.

We cannot now speak of maximizing the value of the objective function, since this function is now known only in a probabilistic sense. We can, however, maximize its expected value. For a single stage we may define

$$f_1(\mathbf{p}_2) = \text{Max} \int P(\mathbf{p}_1)\, dG(\mathbf{p}_2,\mathbf{p}_1;\mathbf{q}_1) \tag{1}$$

where the maximization is by choice of $\mathbf{q}_1$. We thus have an optimal policy which maximizes the expected value of the objective function for a given $\mathbf{p}_2$. If we consider a process in which the outcome of one stage is known before passage to the next, then the principle of optimality shows that the policy in subsequent stages should be optimal with respect to the outcome of the first. Then

$$f_R(\mathbf{p}_{R+1}) = \text{Max} \int f_{R-1}(\mathbf{p}_R)\, dG(\mathbf{p}_{R+1},\mathbf{p}_R;\mathbf{q}_R), \tag{2}$$

the maximization being over all admissible $\mathbf{q}_R$ and the integration over the whole of stage space.

The type of presentation of results used in the deterministic process may be used here, except that now the fourth column is redundant. The third column gives the optimal policy, but we must wait to see the outcome of stage $R$ and enter the preceding section of the table at this state. The discussion of the optimal policy when the outcome of one stage is not known before passing to the next is a very much more difficult matter.

## 2.4. The Continuous Deterministic Process

In many cases it is not possible to divide the process into a finite number of discrete stages, since the state of the stream is transformed in a continuous manner through the process. We replace $r$, the number of the stage from the end of the process, by $t$, a continuous variable which measures the "distance" of the point considered from the end of the process. The word *distance* is used here in a rather general sense; it may in fact be the time that will elapse before the end of the process. If $T$ is the total "length" of the process, its

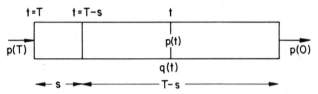

FIG. 2.2. The continuous process.

feed state may be denoted by a vector $\mathbf{p}(T)$ and the product state by $\mathbf{p}(0)$. $\mathbf{p}(t)$ denotes the state at any point $t$ and $\mathbf{q}(t)$ the vector of operating variables there. Figure 2.2 illustrates this.

The process is deterministic in the sense that given the value of $\mathbf{q}(t)$ on any interval $(\sigma, \tau)$, $0 \leq \sigma < \tau \leq T$, the value of $\mathbf{p}(\sigma)$ is uniquely determined by that of $\mathbf{p}(\tau)$. We write

$$\mathbf{p}(\sigma) = \Im\{\mathbf{p}(\tau), \tau - \sigma; \mathbf{q}(t)\},$$

$$0 \leq \sigma \leq t \leq \tau \leq T \qquad (1)$$

and in particular the product state is obtained from the feed state when $\mathbf{q}(t)$ is specified for $0 \leq t \leq T$,

$$\mathbf{p}(0) = \Im\{\mathbf{p}(T), T; \mathbf{q}(t)\}. \qquad (2)$$

Just as in the discrete case, an objective function can be set up as some function of the product state, $P[\mathbf{p}(0)]$. Then the optimal policy is that admissible function $\mathbf{q}(t)$, $0 \leq t \leq T$, which maximizes $P[\mathbf{p}(0)]$.

Let

$$f[\mathbf{p}(T), T] = \text{Max } P[\mathbf{p}(0)] \qquad (3)$$

where $\mathbf{p}(0)$ is given by (2) and the maximization is over all admissible $\mathbf{q}(t)$, $0 \leq t \leq T$. By the principle of optimality we see that whatever choice of $\mathbf{q}$ may be made in the interval $(T - s, T)$ the optimal policy must be used in the remaining interval $(T - s, 0)$ with respect to the state $\mathbf{p}(T - s)$. Thus

$$f[\mathbf{p}(T), T] = \text{Max } f[\mathbf{p}(T - s), T - s],$$

$$0 \leq s \leq T \qquad (4)$$

where

$$\mathbf{p}(T - s) = \Im\{\mathbf{p}(T), s; \mathbf{q}(t)\} \tag{5}$$

and the maximization is over all admissible functions $\mathbf{q}(t)$ in the interval $T - s \leq t \leq T$.

If $f$ and $\Im$ are differentiable and the arbitrary length $s$ is allowed to become very small so that

$$f[\mathbf{p}(T - s), T - s] = f[\mathbf{p}(T), T] - s\left\{\frac{\partial f}{\partial \mathbf{p}}\frac{d\mathbf{p}}{dt} + \frac{\partial f}{\partial T}\right\} + O(s^2)$$

then (4) becomes in the limit as $s \to 0$

$$\frac{\partial f}{\partial T} = \text{Max}\left\{-\frac{\partial f}{\partial \mathbf{p}}\frac{d\mathbf{p}}{dt}\right\} \tag{6}$$

$d\mathbf{p}/dt$ is the differential form of the transformation $\Im$, and the expression on the right is the scalar product. The derivatives $d\mathbf{p}/dt$ are to be evaluated at $t = T$, and hence in the maximization only $\mathbf{q}(T)$, a single vector not a vector function, has to be chosen.

## 2.5. *The Dynamic Programming Approach to the Calculus of Variations*

The particular form in which the continuous deterministic process will arise is precisely the new formalism of the calculus of variations that Bellman has propounded in his book (1957). We seek the maximum of the integral of some function of $\mathbf{p}(t)$ and $\mathbf{q}(t)$,

$$\int_0^T F(\mathbf{p}, \mathbf{q})\, dt = \int_0^T F(p_1 \ldots p_n; q_1 \ldots q_m)\, dt. \tag{1}$$

The transformation $\Im$ of the preceding Section is the integral of the system of differential equations

$$\frac{d\mathbf{p}}{dt} = \mathbf{G}(\mathbf{p}; \mathbf{q}) \tag{2}$$

subject to the initial conditions

$$\mathbf{p}(T) = \mathbf{u}. \tag{3}$$

The vector $\mathbf{G}$ depends on the operating policy $\mathbf{q}$, and an optimal policy is one which maximizes the integral (1). The admissible policies will be defined by some set of restrictions, as may also the state

21

variables. In the form in which we need them, these will nearly always be inequalities

$$\mathbf{u}_* \leq \mathbf{p}(t) \leq \mathbf{u}^* \tag{4}$$

$$\mathbf{v}_* \leq \mathbf{q}(t) \leq \mathbf{v}^* \tag{5}$$

We recognize that when the choice of operating policy has been made, the integral is a function only of the initial state $\mathbf{u}$ and the length of the process $T$. Let

$$f(\mathbf{u},T) = \text{Max} \int_0^T F(\mathbf{p};\mathbf{q})\, dt \tag{6}$$

where the maximization is by choice of $\mathbf{q}(t)$ subject to Eq. (5), and $\mathbf{p}$ is related to $\mathbf{q}$ by Eqs. (3) and (4). The integral may be written

$$\int_{T-s}^T F\, dt + \int_0^{T-s} F\, dt$$

and by the principle of optimality the optimal policy with respect to the state $\mathbf{p}(T - s)$ must certainly be used in the second integral. Thus

$$f(\mathbf{u},T) = \text{Max} \left\{ \int_{T-s}^T F(\mathbf{p},\mathbf{q})\, dt + f[\mathbf{p}(T - s), T - s] \right\} \tag{7}$$

for any $s$, $0 \leq s \leq T$, where the maximization is over admissible $\mathbf{q}(t)$, $(T - s) \leq t \leq T$. In the limit as $s \to 0$

$$f[\mathbf{p}(T - s),T - s] = f(\mathbf{u},T) - s \left\{ \frac{\partial f}{\partial \mathbf{u}} \frac{d\mathbf{p}}{dt} + \frac{\partial f}{\partial T} \right\} + O(s^2)$$

where $d\mathbf{p}/dt$ is evaluated at $t = T$ and so is $\mathbf{G}(\mathbf{u},\mathbf{v})$, $\mathbf{v}$ being the choice of $\mathbf{q}(T)$. Thus in the limit

$$\frac{\partial f}{\partial T} = \text{Max} \left\{ F(\mathbf{u},\mathbf{v}) - \frac{\partial f}{\partial \mathbf{u}} \mathbf{G}(\mathbf{u},\mathbf{v}) \right\} \tag{8}$$

where the maximization is over all admissible $\mathbf{q}(T) = \mathbf{v}$. Again, the second term on the right is understood to be a scalar product $\sum_{i=1}^{n} (\partial f/\partial u_i) G_i(\mathbf{u},\mathbf{v})$.

This is a first-order, quasi-linear partial differential equation, although the presence of the maximization gives it an unconventional form. It must be integrated subject to the boundary condition

$$f(\mathbf{u},0) \equiv 0 \tag{9}$$

which implies that

$$\frac{\partial f}{\partial u_i} = 0 \qquad\qquad i = 1, \ldots n \qquad (10)$$

$$\frac{\partial f}{\partial T} = \text{Max } F(\mathbf{u},\mathbf{v}) \qquad\qquad (11)$$

Bellman (1957) has suggested that the equation may be integrated by a finite difference technique ("Dynamic Programming," p. 254), but he acknowledges the likelihood of computational difficulties and is led to formulate a discrete version of the problem. Fortunately, in the case we shall be concerned with the method of characteristics is well suited to the integration of these equations.

To illustrate how this works, let us suppose that there is only one operating variable, of which the right-hand side of (8) is always a unimodal function. Special as this may seem, it is the important case in Chapter 7. Let us denote $\partial f/\partial T$ by $f_T$, $\partial f/\partial u_i$ by $f_i$, and use the summation convention on the repeated index $i = 1, \ldots n$. Then Eq. (8) may take one of three forms:

$$f_T = \begin{cases} F(\mathbf{u},v_*) - f_i G_i(\mathbf{u},v_*) \\ F(\mathbf{u},v) - f_i G_i(\mathbf{u},v) \\ F(\mathbf{u},v^*) - f_i G_i(\mathbf{u},v^*) \end{cases} \qquad (12)$$

according as the single maximum lies to the left within, or to the right of the interval $(v_*,v^*)$. In the second case $v$ satisfies the equation

$$F_{,v} - f_i G_{i,v} = 0 \qquad\qquad (13)$$

and is a function of $f_i$ and $u_i$ calculable from this equation. (The suffix $,v$ denotes partial differentiation with respect to $v$.)

In the first and last cases the characteristic equations are immediately written down as

$$\frac{du_j}{ds} = G_j(\mathbf{u},v) \qquad\qquad j = 1, \ldots n \qquad (14)$$

$$\frac{dT}{ds} = 1 \qquad\qquad (15)$$

$$\frac{df}{ds} = F(\mathbf{u},v) \qquad\qquad (16)$$

$$\frac{df_j}{ds} = F_{,j} - f_i G_{i,j} \qquad\qquad j = 1, \ldots n \qquad (17)$$

$$\frac{df_T}{ds} = 0 \qquad\qquad (18)$$

23

where $s$ is the variable along the characteristic and $v$ takes the value $v_*$ or $v^*$, and $G_{i,j}$ denotes $\partial G_i/\partial u_j$. Of course in this case Eqs. (17) and (18) are not needed, for dividing (14) by (15) we have

$$\frac{du_j}{dT} = G_j(\mathbf{u},v)$$

which is just another form of Eq. (2).[†] Combining Eqs. (15) and (16) likewise leads to Eq. (1).

In deriving the characteristic equations for $v_* \le v \le v^*$, we have to take account of the fact that $v$ is a function of $f_i$ and $u_i$ so that, for example,

$$\frac{du_j}{ds} = \frac{\partial}{\partial f_j}(f_T + f_iG_i - F) = G_j + (f_iG_i - F)_{,v}\frac{\partial v}{\partial f_j}.$$

But since $v$ satisfies Eq. (13), this reduces to Eq. (14). In fact the characteristic equations are still given by (14)–(18), but now $v$ satisfies Eq. (13). We can differentiate this equation along the characteristic and so obtain an equation for $v$, namely,

$$\frac{dv}{ds} = \frac{(F_{,j}G_{j,v} - G_jF_{,jv}) - f_i(G_{i,j}G_{j,v} - G_jG_{i,jv})}{F_{,vv} - f_iG_{i,vv}} \tag{19}$$

So long as $v_* \le v \le v^*$ this equation can be carried along with Eqs. (14)–(18) and the optimal policy can be obtained simultaneously with the trajectory and the objective function.

Equation (18), though apparently trivial, is actually rather useful. It shows that $f_T$ does not change along a characteristic. Since we are seeking a maximum we are certainly not interested in a process which is so long that $f_T$ is negative. Thus Eq. (18) assures us that by integrating along characteristics for which $f_T > 0$ on the initial plane $T = 0$ we shall generate the solution in the only part of $(u,T)$-space which is of importance.

In fact, Eq. (19) proves to be the best way of keeping track of $v$. The initial plane $T = 0$ will be divided into three regions according as the maximum of $F(\mathbf{u},v)$ is in the interval $(-\infty,v_*)$, $(v_*,v^*)$, or $(v^*,\infty)$. A characteristic emanating from the second of these regions is found by integrating Eqs. (14)–(19) with initial values given by

---

† Had the variable $t$ or $T$ been given its positive sense in the same direction as the stream, Eq. (19) would be changed in sign from (2). It is consistent with our numbering of the discrete stages to have $t$ reckoned from the end, and it will prove, as before, an advantage in extracting the optimum policy.

Eqs. (9)–(11) and the $v$ that makes $F$ maximum. The integration proceeds until either one of the inequalities (4) is violated or until $v$ reaches $v_*$ or $v^*$. Suppose that $v = v^*$ at a point of the characteristic; then the equations (14), (15), and (16) with $v = v^*$ will have to be solved as we continue along the characteristic until such time as either one of the inequalities (14) is violated or the optimal $v$ becomes less than $v^*$ again. We can always find out if the latter possibility came about by testing the root of Eq. (13) to see in which interval it lies. However, if we continue to use Eq. (19) as the derivative of (18) along a characteristic, (19) will keep track of the root of Eq. (12) and show us when $v$ comes back into the interval $(v_*, v^*)$ again. This must be done a little carefully, for Eq. (19) is obtained from

$$0 = \frac{d}{ds}(F_{,v} - f_i G_{i,v})$$

$$= (F_{,vv} - f_i G_{i,vv})\frac{dv}{ds} + (F_{,jv} - f_i G_{i,jv})\frac{du_j}{ds} - G_{i,v}\frac{df_i}{ds}$$

and along a characteristic with $v = v^*$, for example

$$\frac{du_j}{ds} = G_j^*, \qquad \frac{df_i}{ds} = F_{,i}^* - f_j G_{j,i}^*$$

where the asterisk denotes that $v$ has been put equal to $v^*$. Thus Eq. (19) becomes (after a slight rearrangement of dummy suffices)

$$\frac{dv}{ds} = \frac{(F_{,j}^* G_{j,v} - G_j^* F_{,jv}) - f_i(G_{i,j}^* G_{j,v} - G_j^* G_{i,jv})}{F_{,vv} - f_i G_{i,vv}}. \qquad (19^*)$$

A similar equation $(19_*)$ applies when $v = v_*$. When the characteristic emanates from a region of the initial plane $T = 0$ where $v = v^*$, we may determine the root $v_m$ of Eq. (13) and use this as the initial value in the characteristic Eq. $(19^*)$. Then when the value of $v$ given by this equation decreases to $v^*$, the characteristic equations (14)–(19) are resumed.

The process may be described as follows. We denote the three intervals $(-\infty, v_*)$, $(v_*, v^*)$, and $(v^*, \infty)$ by $I_1$, $I_2$, and $I_3$ respectively, and the three regions of the initial plane $T = 0$ for which $v_m$ lies in $I_1$, $I_2$, or $I_3$ by $D_1$, $D_2$, and $D_3$ respectively. By integration in the mode $M_2$ we mean the integration of the characteristic equations (14)–(19), and by integration in modes $M_1$ and $M_3$ we mean that $v$ should be set at $v_*$ or $v^*$ in (14)–(18), and Eq. $(19_*)$ or $(19^*)$ should replace (19). Then the rule is simply to integrate in the mode $M_j$ which corresponds to the interval $I_j$ in which $v$ lies, and to start in the mode $M_i$ if the characteristic emanates from $D_i$. Such a program is well adapted to machine computation.

This method may be extended to the case $m > 1$, but the practical difficulty of establishing the monotonicity of $F_{,v} - f_i G_{i,v}$ becomes severe in the general case. However easy it may be for a mathematician to construct a counterexample, the smoothness that obtains in many physical situations gives the method its interest and value, as will be shown in later examples.

If we are looking for the optimal policy for a process of length $T$ with feed state $\mathbf{p}(T)$, a certain amount of trial and error must be employed, for there is no way of starting the equations from the inlet condition $\mathbf{p}(T)$. The initial conditions for the integration are given only on $T = 0$, and we must seek out the characteristic emanating from this plane that passes through the given point $[\mathbf{p}(T),T]$. There is indeed the possibility that the point may not lie in the region for which $\partial f/\partial T$ is positive, in which case a greater value of the objective function could be obtained with the same initial state $\mathbf{p}$ but different $T$. If we seek also the optimal $T$ then we need the characteristic through $\mathbf{p}$, $T$ for which $f_T = 0$. This is easier to find, for the value of $f_T$ is constant along a characteristic so that it emanates from a point on the initial plane $T = 0$ for which $f_T = \max F(\mathbf{u},v) = 0$. Something of the same trial and error is needed in other methods of solving this problem. Thus Katz (1960a,b) has used the classical techniques and arrived at a two-point boundary condition for the characteristics, which again requires a trial-and-error solution. Amundson and Bilous (1956) have the same set of equations which they integrate from the feed condition, but they do not know ahead of time for what length of process this will be optimum. This case is discussed below in Sections 7.3 and 7.4, where it is shown that it arises only if $n = 2$ and $F$ is independent of $v$.

## 2.6. *The Use and Interpretation of the Lagrange Multiplier*

The notion of the undetermined multiplier was introduced into classical analysis by Lagrange to handle a variational problem with constraints. For example, if we seek the unrestricted maximum of the

26

function $f(x_1, \ldots x_n)$, the classical technique is to solve the simultaneous equations $\partial f / \partial x_i = 0$, $i = 1, \ldots n$. If the variables are restricted by some relation $g(x_1, \ldots x_n) = 0$ we could in principle solve this and obtain $x_1, \ldots x_{n-1}$ as functions of $x_n$. Then $f$ would be a function of only $(n - 1)$ variables and the maximum would be found by solution of $\partial f / \partial x_i = 0$, $i = 1, \ldots (n - 1)$. However, it is often better to seek the unrestrained maximum of $f - \lambda g$ by solving the equations $\partial (f - \lambda g) / \partial x_i = 0$, $i = 1, \ldots n$. Of course the values of $x_1, \ldots x_n$ so found will depend on $\lambda$ and so $g(x_1, \ldots x_n)$ for these values will be a function $G(\lambda)$. It now suffices to determine the $\lambda$ for which $G(\lambda) = 0$, and the restricted maximum of $f$ is found. The same notion may be used to advantage with dynamic programming, as the following examples will show.

Suppose we have a discrete deterministic process with one state variable $p$ and one operating variable $q$. Let $P(p_1) = p_1 - p_{R+1} = \sum_1^R (p_r - p_{r+1})$ be the objective function to be maximized, subject to the restriction $\sum_1^R q_r = Q$. The relation between $p_{r+1}$ and $p_r$ is $p_r = \mathfrak{Z}(p_{r+1};q_r)$, as in Eq. (2.1). There are two ways of formulating this problem. In the first we recognize that the maximum of the objective function will depend on both $p_{R+1}$ and $Q$, and we set

$$f_R(p_{R+1},Q) = \operatorname{Max} \sum_1^R (p_r - p_{r+1}) \tag{1}$$

the maximum being over all admissible $q_r$, $r = 1, \ldots R$, subject to

$$\sum_1^R q_r = Q. \tag{2}$$

Then the principle of optimality yields the functional equation

$$f_R(p_{R+1},Q) = \operatorname{Max} [(p_R - p_{R+1}) + f_{R-1}(p_R,Q - q_R)] \tag{3}$$

where the maximization is over all admissible $q_R$ for which $0 \le q_R \le Q$. In solving the problem in this form a function $f_r$ of two variables has to be computed and stored in passing from stage to stage.

An alternative formulation is to seek the maximum of $P(p_1) - \lambda \sum_1^R q_r$, which for any fixed $\lambda$ will depend only on $p_{R+1}$. Let

$$g_{R,\lambda}(p_{R+1}) = \operatorname{Max} \sum_1^R (p_r - p_{r+1} - \lambda q_r). \tag{4}$$

27

Then the principle of optimality gives

$$g_{R,\lambda}(p_{R+1}) = \text{Max}\,[p_R - p_{R+1} - \lambda g_R + g_{R-1,\lambda}(p_R)] \qquad (5)$$

where the maximization is over all admissible $q_R$. Here for any particular $\lambda$ a function $g_r$ of only one variable is taken from stage to stage. This very greatly reduces the requirements of storage and interpolation, and it is quicker to solve a number of such problems for various $\lambda$ than to solve the problem in its first formulation, for $Q_R(\lambda) = \sum_1^R q_r$ can be calculated any value of $\lambda$, and the original problem is solved by that value of $\lambda$ for which $Q_R(\lambda) = Q$.

The same treatment is useful for the continuous process. If we had an analogous problem such as finding the maximum of

$$\int_0^T F(p,q)\,dt \qquad (6)$$

with

$$\frac{dp}{dt} = G(p,q), p(T) = u \qquad (7)$$

and

$$\int_0^T H(q)\,dt = H \qquad (8)$$

the direct formulation would require us to set

$$f(u,T,H) = \text{Max} \int_0^T F(p,q)\,dt. \qquad (9)$$

This would lead to the partial differential equation

$$f_T = \text{Max}\,\{F(u,v) - f_u G(u,v) - f_H H(v)\} \qquad (10)$$

the maximum being over all admissible $q(T) = v$. Here we have an equation in three independent variables and for a given feed state $p(T) = u$, length of process $T$, and constant $H$ we have to hit the point $(u,v,T)$ in [3] space. The same problem could however be formulated with the use of a Lagrange multiplier, by seeking the maximum

$$g_\lambda(u,T) = \text{Max} \int_0^T \{F(p,q) - \lambda H(q)\}\,dt. \qquad (11)$$

In this case we are led to the partial differential equation

$$g_T = \text{Max}\,\{F(u,v) - \lambda H(v) - g_u G(u,v)\} \qquad (12)$$

in only two independent variables. Given the feed state and process

28

length, it is far easier to hit the point $(u, T)$ in [2] space. For this solution

$$H(\lambda) = \int_0^T H(q) \, dt \qquad (13)$$

will be determined for one value of $\lambda$, and the original problem will be solved by the value of $\lambda$ that makes $H(\lambda) = H$. It is true that this requires another process of trial and error, but even in this case it may be an easier way to get at the required solution, and for a greater number of restrictions the advantage will probably be more noticeable. Bellman (1956) gave a general introduction to the value of such methods, which have been used in many contexts.

The Lagrange multiplier has also a simple and instructive interpretation: In the above examples it is a certain measure of the cost involved in the use of the operating policy. Thus it is easy to see in the first example that the greater the value of $\lambda$ the smaller will be the total sum $Q_R(\lambda)$ (this is shown in Fig. 2.3), for $p_1 - p_{R+1} - \lambda \sum_1^R q_r$ is the "profit" from the transformation minus the "cost" of the operating variables $q_r$. In some cases we may have both a restriction

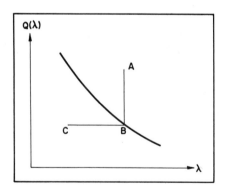

Fig. 2.3. Illustrating the interpretation of the Lagrange multiplier.

$Q$ and an estimate of the cost $\lambda$. If the point $(\lambda, Q)$ lies above the curve (as does A in Fig. 2.3), this implies that the cost is so great that this, rather than the restriction $Q$, is the real limitation, for the optimum for this value of $\lambda$ lies at B on the curve below A where not all the available $Q$ can be used. In contrast, if $(\lambda, Q)$ is located as C, it is the restriction $Q$ which is dominant and this implies that $Q$ acquires a scarcity value ($\lambda$ at B) which is greater than its real value.

# 3

# Mathematical Models for Reactor Design

---

*. . . It next will be right*
*To describe each particular batch:*
*Distinguishing those that have feathers, and bite,*
*From those that have whiskers, and scratch.*

---

IN THIS CHAPTER we shall set up the equations that are needed for the optimal design problems to be described later. It is convenient to group the principal types of reactors at this point, for some understanding of their defining equations is desirable before discussing the way in which the optimum problem is formulated. We are not greatly concerned with setting up the most complete and detailed representation of a particular reactor; it is sufficient, and even desirable, to have the simplest adequate set of equations. Nor will we later always attempt to solve the most general problem, for principles are best exhibited when free from overmuch detail. It is hoped that it will become clear to the reader that the methods are not in any way limited to relatively simple models and problems; much more detailed descriptions and accurate cost and profit estimates may be used, and their success requires only the patience to program them. It should be remembered however that certain items, such as kinetic constants, can never be known to as great an accuracy as the designer would wish, and it is futile to burden the problem with a superstructure of fallacious accuracy which its foundations cannot bear.

We shall adopt the convention in this and later chapters that the unqualified word *reactor*, occurring in any section or chapter specifically devoted to a certain type of reactor, will signify that particular type. Any other type referred to will be suitably qualified.

## 3.1. Systems of Chemical Reactions

Let $A_i$, $i = 1, \ldots n$, denote the chemical species which are taking part in a system of $m$ reactions. The equations for these reactions may be written

$$\sum_{i=1}^{n} \alpha_{ij} A_i = 0, \qquad j = 1, \ldots m, \tag{1}$$

where $\alpha_{ij}$ is the stoichiometric coefficient of $A_i$ in the $j$th reaction. We observe the convention that those species which are regarded as products in any reaction should have positive stoichiometric coefficients. Thus, for example, two of the reactions present in methanol synthesis,

$$CO + 2H_2 = CH_3OH$$
$$CO_2 + H_2 = CO + H_2O$$

can be rewritten

$$A_1 - A_2 - 2A_3 \qquad\qquad = 0$$
$$A_2 - A_3 - A_4 + A_5 = 0$$

by taking $A_1$ to be $CH_3OH$, $A_2 = CO$, $A_3 = H_2$, $A_4 = CO_2$, and $A_5 = H_2O$. Then the matrix of stoichiometric coefficients is

$$\alpha' \equiv \begin{Vmatrix} 1 & -1 & -2 & . & . \\ . & 1 & -1 & -1 & 1 \end{Vmatrix}.$$

We shall assume that the reactions are independent, i.e., that none of them can be expressed as a linear combination of the others. More precisely, we say that there exists no set of $m$ numbers $\lambda_1, \ldots \lambda_m$, except the trivial set $\lambda_1 = \lambda_2 = \ldots = \lambda_m = 0$, such that

$$\sum_{j=1}^{m} \alpha_{ij} \lambda_j = 0. \tag{2}$$

If we are given any set of reactions not necessarily linearly independent, it is always possible to reduce them to a set of equivalent

32

reactions which are linearly independent, and we assume that this has been done. There are now two ways of ensuring that we need work with only $m$ equations to describe the concentration changes of the $n$ species, and since both have their uses we will describe them both.

In the first we associate an extent or degree of advancement with each reaction. Suppose that at the start of the reaction $N_{i0}$ moles of $A_i$ are present; then if $N_{ij}$ moles of $A_i$ react in the $j$th reaction, $N_{kj} = \alpha_{kj} N_{ij}/\alpha_{ij}$ moles of $A_k$ must also react, for this is the meaning of the equation $\sum \alpha_{ij} A_i = 0$. Thus

$$N^j = \frac{N_{kj}}{\alpha_{kj}} = \frac{N_{ij}}{\alpha_{ij}}, \qquad i,k = 1, \ldots n$$

is independent of the species for the $j$th reaction. This may be called the extent of the $j$th reaction, and it is evident that the change in the number of moles of $A_i$ when there is a change of extent $N^j$ is $N_{ij} = \alpha_{ij} N^j$. If the reactions proceed to extents $N^1, N^2, \ldots N^m$, then the total change in the number of moles of $A_i$ is $\sum_{j=1}^{m} \alpha_{ij} N^j$, and if $N_i$ is the number of moles of $A_i$ then present,

$$N_i = N_{i0} + \sum_{j=1}^{m} \alpha_{ij} N^j. \tag{3}$$

Since the total mass of the reacting mixture will not change, we may divide this equation by it and obtain

$$g_i = g_{i0} + \sum_{j=1}^{m} \alpha_{ij} g^j, \tag{4}$$

where $g_i$ is the concentration of $A_i$ in moles per unit mass of mixture, $g_{i0}$ the initial concentration of $A_i$, and $g^j$ the extent of the $j$th reaction in this unit. If the reaction takes place at constant volume, Eq. (3) can be divided by this volume to give

$$c_i = c_{i0} + \sum_{j=1}^{m} \alpha_{ij} c^j, \tag{5}$$

where concentration and extent are now measured in units of moles per unit volume. Since reaction rates for homogeneous reactions are normally given in moles per unit time per unit volume, this last will be taken as the standard unit of measure. If $\rho$ is the density of the reacting mixture,

$$c_i = \rho g_i. \tag{6}$$

33

This allows the concentration units to be changed to suit the problem, and other measures of concentration, such as mole fraction, partial pressure, or fugacity, might be introduced. $g$ is a good measure to use for gaseous reactions with volume changes and will be mentioned later in connection with tubular reactors; otherwise we will phrase our problems in terms of $c$, recognizing that this implies no limitation on the method.

The rate of the $j$th reaction will be defined as the rate of change of $c^j$ by reaction alone, and we take this to be a known function of the local thermodynamic state

$$(dc^j/dt)_r = r^j(c_1, \ldots c_n, p, T). \tag{7}$$

By means of the relations (5) we can express the concentrations in terms of the extents, and have

$$r^j = r^j(c^1, \ldots c^m, p, T; c_{10}, \ldots c_{n0}) = r^j(c^k, p, T). \tag{8}$$

Then the rate of change of concentration of $A_i$ due to reaction alone is

$$\left(\frac{dc_i}{dt}\right)_r = \sum_{j=1}^{m} \alpha_{ij} r^j. \tag{9}$$

The use of the extent of reaction has a certain symmetry, associating one variable with the progress of each reaction. If we are considering a system of reactions in which one or more of the reactions are negligible, we have only to set the corresponding $r^j$ equal to zero. However, if the final answer is needed in concentrations, Eqs. (5) must be used to get back from the extents. Thus it is sometimes preferable to work in terms of the concentrations of certain key components of the reaction mixture.* Since the reactions are independent we can always name the species in such a way that the leading submatrix of order $m \times m$ in the matrix $\alpha$ of stoichiometric coefficients is nonsingular. In fact, by dividing each column of $\alpha$ by the corresponding element of the leading diagonal we can make this a unit diagonal. The first $m$ species, $A_1, \ldots A_m$, may then be taken as the key components and the concentrations of the others expressed in terms of theirs.

---

* A circumstance in which this formulation has a very definite advantage is the simultaneous diffusion and reaction that takes place within a catalyst pellet. However, we shall not have occasion to advert to this.

Thus we may rewrite Eqs. (3) as follows:

$$\alpha_{11}N^1 + \ldots + \alpha_{1m}N^m = N_1 - N_{10}$$

.
.
.

$$\alpha_{m1}N^1 + \ldots + \alpha_{mm}N^m = N_m - N_{m0}$$

$$\alpha_{m+1,1}N^1 + \ldots + \alpha_{m+1,m}N^m = N_{m+1} - N_{m+1,0}$$

.
.
.

$$\alpha_{n1}N^1 + \ldots + \alpha_{nm}N^m = N_n - N_{n0}.$$

Since by arrangement the matrix

$$
\begin{matrix}
\alpha_{11} & \alpha_{12} & \ldots & \alpha_{1m} \\
\alpha_{21} & \alpha_{22} & \ldots & \alpha_{2m} \\
\cdot & \cdot & & \cdot \\
\cdot & \cdot & & \cdot \\
\cdot & \cdot & & \cdot \\
\alpha_{m1} & \alpha_{m2} & \ldots & \alpha_{mm}
\end{matrix}
$$

is nonsingular, the first $m$ of these equations can be solved to give

$$N^j = \sum_{i=1}^{m} \beta_{ji}(N_i - N_{i0}). \tag{10}$$

Then, substituting into the last $(n - m)$ equations,

$$N_k = N_{k0} + \sum_{j=1}^{m} \sum_{i=1}^{m} \alpha_{kj}\beta_{ji}(N_i - N_{i0}),$$
$$k = m + 1, \ldots n \tag{11}$$

which expresses the remaining $N_k$ in terms of the first $m$. Dividing through by the mass or the volume gives a similar relation for the $g_i$ or $c_i$; in particular,

$$c_k = c_{k0} + \sum_{j=1}^{m} \sum_{i=1}^{m} \alpha_{kj}\beta_{ji}(c_i - c_{i0}). \tag{12}$$

Now let $f_i$ be the rate of change of $c_i$ due to all the reactions. This will be a function of all the $c_i$ and $p$ and $T$, but by (12) it may be expressed as a function of $c_1, \ldots c_m, p, T$. Thus

$$f_i = f_i(c_1, \ldots c_n, p, T)$$
$$= f_i(c_1, \ldots c_m, p, T; c_{10}, \ldots c_{n0}) \tag{13}$$
$$= \sum_{j=1}^{m} \alpha_{ij}r^j, \qquad i = 1, \ldots m.$$

Then the rate of formation of the other species is given by

$$f_k = \sum_{j=1}^{m} \sum_{i=1}^{m} \alpha_{kj}\beta_{ji}f_i. \tag{14}$$

In either case the course of the $m$ simultaneous reactions has been expressed in terms of only $m$ functions.

The number of independent reactions is an index of the stoichiometric complexity of the system. As Piret and Trambouze (1959) have pointed out, the expressions $r_j$ or $f_j$ may be found to contain fewer than the $m$ concentrations. In this case it is possible to work with fewer than $m$ equations, but integral, rather than algebraic, relations will be needed to recover the other concentrations. This observation has also been made by Horn (1961).

If $H_i$ is the partial molar enthalpy of $A_i$, then

$$\Delta H_j = \sum_{i=1}^{n} \alpha_{ij}H_i \tag{15}$$

is defined to be the enthalpy or heat of the $j$th reaction. It is the heat absorbed by a unit change in the extent $N^j$, and is positive for an endothermic reaction. Since many of the simpler cases of interest arise from exothermic reactions, we shall often write $(-\Delta H_j)$ and recall that this will then be positive. The rate of generation of sensible heat per unit volume from all the reactions is

$$\sum_{j=1}^{m} (-\Delta H_j)r^j. \tag{16}$$

The system of reactions (1) is said to be in equilibrium when all the rates of reaction are simultaneously zero,

$$r^1 = r^2 = \ldots = r^m = 0. \tag{17}$$

These equations can be solved for the extents at equilibrium $c_e^j$ in terms of the initial composition $c_{i0}$, pressure $p$, and temperature $T$ provided that the Jacobian

$$\frac{\partial(r^1, r^2, \ldots r^m)}{\partial(c^1, c^2, \ldots c^m)}$$

does not vanish.

In the neighborhood of equilibrium all systems of reaction can be described by first-order equations; for supposing that $(c^j - c_e^j)$ is small enough for its squares and products to be neglected, we have

$$\left(\frac{dc^j}{dt}\right)_r = \sum_{k=1}^{m} \left(\frac{\partial r^j}{\partial c^k}\right)_e (c^k - c_e^k).$$

It is commonly asserted that the latent roots of this Jacobian matrix are all real and negative as a consequence of the principle of microscopic reversibility. However, a discussion of this would take us outside the bounds of our subject.

## 3.2. *The Continuous Flow Stirred Tank Reactor*

We turn now to consider the principal types of reactors and derive a set of equations for each that will describe the transformation ℑ of the state of the feed into the state of the product. The continuous flow stirred tank reactor* is one of the simplest in basic design and is widely used in chemical industry. Basically it consists in a vessel of volume $V$ furnished with one or more inlets, an outlet, a means of cooling and a stirrer which keeps its composition and temperature essentially uniform. We shall assume that there is complete mixing on the molecular scale. It would be possible to treat of other cases following the work of Danckwerts (1958) and Zweitering (1959), but the corresponding transformation is much less wieldy. If the reactants flow in and out at a constant rate $q$, the mean residence time $V/q$ is known as the holding time of the reactor.

Let $c_{if}$ be the concentration of $A_i$ in the feed to the reactor, and $c_i$ the concentration in the reactor and hence in the outflowing product. Then a mass balance for $A_i$ gives

$$V \frac{dc_i}{dt} = q(c_{if} - c_i) + V \sum_{j=1}^{m} \alpha_{ij} r^j,$$

$$i = 1, \ldots n. \quad (1)$$

If we are using the second method and express all concentrations in terms of the first $m$, then a sufficient set of equations is given by

$$\theta \frac{dc_i}{dt} = c_{if} - c_i + \theta f_i(c_1, \ldots c_m, T, p)$$

$$i = 1, \ldots m. \quad (2)$$

Here $f_i$ has been written as a function of the $m$ concentrations, the temperature, and pressure. It should also be remembered that a reference composition, $c_{i0}$, is implicit in $f_i$; it is sometimes, but not

---

* So sesquipedalian a style supplicates a sobriquet. It has received "C.F.S.T.R." from Denbigh, "C*" from Piret and "tank" from many others.

usually, possible to identify this with the feed composition. If the extent of reaction be used we have from (3.1.5)* and (1)

$$\sum_1^m \alpha_{ij}\left\{\theta\frac{dc^j}{dt} - c_f^j + c^j - \theta r^j\right\} = 0 \tag{3}$$

where $c_f^j$ is the extent of reaction in the feed

$$c_{if} = c_{i0} + \sum_1^m \alpha_{ij}c_f^j.$$

But by the assumption of the independence of the reactions [Eq. (3.1.2)] the coefficients of the $\alpha_{ij}$ must be identically zero if Eq. (3) holds. Thus

$$\theta\frac{dc^j}{dt} = c_f^j - c^j + \theta r^j(c^1, \ldots c^m, T, p)$$

$$j = 1, \ldots m, \tag{4}$$

which gives a sufficient set of equations in terms of the extents. In particular, in a sequence of stirred tank reactors in which the flow passes from stage $R$ through to stage 1 we may use the suffix $r$ to denote conditions in stage $r$ and, quite consistently, the suffix $(R+1)$ for the feed. Thus

$$\theta_r\frac{dc_r^j}{dt} = c_{r+1}^j - c_r^j + \theta_r r^j(c_r^1, \ldots c_r^m, T_r) \tag{5}$$

or

$$\theta_r\frac{dc_{ir}}{dt} = c_{i,r+1} - c_{ir} + \theta_r f_i(c_{1r}, \ldots c_{nr}, T_r) \tag{6}$$

with $i$ or $j = 1, \ldots m$, $r = 1, \ldots R$.

In what follows we shall not be much concerned with variations in pressure, and so we will write the kinetic expressions as functions of temperature only, as in Eqs. (5) and (6). At constant pressure the energy balance for the reactor becomes an enthalpy balance and, if we write $VQ(t)$ for the rate of heat removal from the reactor, this becomes

$$V\frac{d}{dt}\left(\sum_1^n c_i H_i\right) = q\sum_1^n \{c_{if}H_i(T_f) - c_i H_i(T)\} - VQ.$$

* Equation (5) of Chapter 3, Section 1. Equations in sections other than the immediate one will be referred to in this manner.

But

$$V \frac{d}{dt} \left( \sum_1^n c_i H_i \right) = V \left( \sum_1^n c_i c_{pi} \right) \frac{dT}{dt} + V \sum_1^n H_i \frac{dc_i}{dt}$$

$$= V C_p \frac{dT}{dt} + q \sum (c_{if} - c_i) H_i(T) + V \sum_{i=1}^n \sum_{j=1}^m \alpha_{ij} H_i r^j,$$

where $c_{pi} = \partial H_i / \partial T$ and $C_p = \sum_1^n c_i c_{pi}$ is the heat capacity per unit volume of the reaction mixture. But substituting this into the preceding equation and using the definition (3.1.15) for heat of reaction,

$$V C_p \frac{dT}{dt} = q \sum_1^n c_{if}[H(T_f) - H(T)] + V \sum_1^m (-\Delta H_j) r^j - VQ. \qquad (7)$$

This is the energy equation which with either of Eqs. (2) or (4) constitutes a set of $(m + 1)$ equations in $(m + 1)$ unknowns, the concentrations or extents and temperature. It is commonly assumed that $C_p$ can be taken to be a mean value, so that

$$\sum c_{if}[H(T_f) - H(T)] = C_p(T_f - T)$$

and hence

$$\theta \frac{dT}{dt} = T_f - T + \theta \sum_1^m \frac{(-\Delta H_j)}{C_p} r^j - \frac{\theta}{C_p} Q. \qquad (8)$$

In the steady state these are no longer differential equations. For the sequence we have either

$$c_{r+1}^j - c_r^j + \theta_r r^j(c_r^1, \ldots c_r^m, T_r) = 0 \qquad (9)$$

and

$$T_{r+1} - T_r + \theta_r \sum_{j=1}^m H^j r_r^j - Q_r' = 0 \qquad (10)$$

where

$$H^j = (-\Delta H_j)/C_p, \qquad Q_r' = \theta_r Q/C_p;$$

or we have

$$c_{i,r+1} - c_{ir} + \theta_r f_i(c_{1r}, \ldots c_{mr}, T_r) = 0 \qquad (11)$$

and

$$T_{r+1} - T_r + \theta_r \sum_1^m H'^i f_{ir} - Q_r' = 0, \qquad (12)$$

where

$$H'^i = \sum_{j=1}^m \beta_{ji} H^j = \sum_{j=1}^m \beta_{ji}(-\Delta H_j)/C_p. \qquad (13)$$

39

In the design of a sequence of such reactors, $Q_r$ and $\theta_r$ play the role of the operating variables and the state is specified by the composition and temperature, $c_{ir}$ or $c_r^j$ and $T_r$. Thus the solution of the equation pairs (9) and (10) or (11) and (12) gives the transformation from the feed to the product state at any one stage. A simpler case of considerable importance is that in which we suppose that any temperature within certain limits can be attained at a given stage. Then the state can be specified by the $m$ composition variables, and the operating variables are $T_r$ and $\theta_r$. In this case only Eq. (9) or (11) is needed to define the transformation and Eq. (10) or (12) is then used to calculate the rate of heat removal to maintain the optimal temperature.

A case of some interest arises when the process stream does not pass unchanged from stage to stage but is mixed with a new reactant stream between stages. An equivalent situation occurs when not only is there a stream passing from stage to stage but also fresh streams entering each reactor; here the mixing is done within the reactor. If the side streams are not of the same reference composition $c_{i0}$ as the process stream, then the situation is messy, for it will be recalled that $c_{i0}$ is implicit in the functions $r^j$ or $f_i$. However, if the reference and side stream compositions are identical, which would be the case if the same basic feed stock were used for the side streams, then the situation is simpler. Suppose that before entering reactor $r$ the feed in state $c_{r+1}^j, T_{r+1}$ or $c_{i,r+1}, T_{r+1}$ is mixed with a stream in state $c_0^j, T_0$. Then if $q_{r+1}$ and $q_r'$ are the flow rates from reactor $(r+1)$ and of the sidestream respectively, we have

$$q_r = q_{r+1} + q_r' \tag{14}$$

for the flow rate through reactor $r$, and the $c_{r+1}^j$, $c_{i,r+1}$, and $T_{r+1}$ of Eqs. (9)–(12) should be replaced by

$$\bar{c}_{r+1}^j = \mu_{r+1} c_{r+1}^j + (1 - \mu_{r+1}) c_0^j \tag{15}$$

$$\bar{c}_{i,r+1} = \mu_{r+1} c_{i,r+1} + (1 - \mu_{r+1}) c_{i0} \tag{16}$$

$$\bar{T}_{r+1} = \mu_{r+1} T_{r+1} + (1 - \mu_{r+1}) T_0 \tag{17}$$

where
$$\mu_{r+1} = q_{r+1}/q_r. \tag{18}$$

## 3.3. The Multibed Adiabatic Reactor

If a stage of a reactor is insulated as far as possible from direct transfer of heat it is called adiabatic. Thus a sequence of stirred tanks with $Q_r = 0$ might be called an adiabatic reactor sequence. We prefer, however, to consider such a sequence in the section on stirred tank reactors, and treat under the present heading the adiabatic reactor whose stages are packed catalyst beds. For these we shall take the simplest of models, but if it is so desired the more detailed considerations of the next section may be taken into account. We assume, then, that there is uniform flow through a reaction bed with negligible longitudinal diffusion, pressure drop, or heat loss. The expressions $r^j$ or $f_i$ are reaction rates per unit volume of the reactor, and the $c^j$ or $c_i$ are concentrations in this unit. This means that for heterogeneous catalysis the various steps (mass transfer, internal diffusion, adsorption, etc.) have already been analyzed and their effect incorporated in the expressions for the reaction rate.

If $A$ is the cross-sectional area of the reactor, $q$ the volume flow rate, and $x$ the distance from the inlet of the bed, a mass balance for the component $A_i$ over an elementary length of bed gives

$$q \frac{dc_i}{dx} = A f_i(c_1, \ldots c_m, T).$$

For simplicity let

$$t = Ax/q \tag{1}$$

be the measure of distance down the bed; then

$$\frac{dc_i}{dt} = f_i(c_k, T). \tag{2}$$

Alternatively, substituting from (3.1.5) and (3.1.13) and again using the fact that the reactions are independent,

$$\frac{dc^j}{dt} = r^j(c^k, T). \tag{3}$$

Since we have neglected pressure drop, the condition that the bed be adiabatic is

$$\frac{d}{dt} \left( \sum_1^n c_i H_i \right) = 0$$

or

$$\sum_1^n c_i H_i(T) = \sum_1^n c_{if} H_i(T_f) \tag{4}$$

which defines $T$ in terms of the $c_i$ throughout the bed when the feed condition $c_{if}$, $T_f$ has been specified. Equation (4) may be rewritten

$$\sum_1^n c_{if} \{ H_i(T) - H_i(T_f) \} = \sum_1^n (c_{if} - c_i) H_i(T)$$

41

and making the same assumption about the validity of a mean specific heat $C_p$ and using (3.1.5), (3.1.15), and (3.2.13),

$$T - T_f = \sum_1^m H^j(c^j - c_f^j)$$

$$= \sum_1^m H'^i(c_i - c_{if}).$$

(5)

Thus the relationship between temperature and extent of reaction is linear if the $H^j$ are constant. This is a very tolerable approximation in many cases, and when it is not so we must go back to (4). In either case we can substitute for $T$ in Eq. (2) or (3) and have a set of $m$ simultaneous first-order differential equations to be solved subject to

$$c^j = c_f^j \quad \text{or} \quad c_i = c_{if} \quad \text{at } t = 0.$$

(6)

The solution of these equations gives the composition and temperature in terms of the feed state and $\theta$, the value of $t$ at the end of the bed. Now in an adiabatic reactor the natural trend of temperature is always unfavorable. For an exothermic reaction the temperature rises, the equilibrium conversion falling with increasing temperature, and vice versa for an endothermic reaction. The advantage of building the reactor in a number of stages and cooling or heating the reactant stream between stages is therefore very great. The cooling in the case of an exothermic reaction is either by interchanger or by mixing with a certain fraction of cold unreacted feed. There are thus two operating variables for each stage, for given a feed of a certain composition and temperature we must first decide to what temperature to cool or heat it and then to what extent to react it; this will fix $T_f$ and $\theta$. In the case of interchanger cooling the choice of inlet temperature will fix the design of the interchanger, while in the other case it will fix the proportion of cold shot. Clearly, good judgment is needed in these choices. If we think in terms of an exothermic reaction with a feed unsuitably near equilibrium, insufficient cooling will not remove this defect whereas too much cooling will quench the reaction. Again, the point at which the increasing bed volume required for increased conversion becomes unprofitable must be nicely judged.

In the case of a single reaction, a graphical representation exhibits the general features of this type of reactor rather well. We will consider the exothermic case since this is more interesting, and drop the affix $j = 1$. Then Eqs. (3) and (5) become

$$\frac{dc}{dt} = r(c,T) \tag{7}$$

$$T = T_f + H(c - c_f). \tag{8}$$

In the plane with coordinates $c$ and $T$ shown in Fig. 3.1 the locus of points for which $r(c,T) = 0$ is the curve $\Gamma_e$. The relation (8),

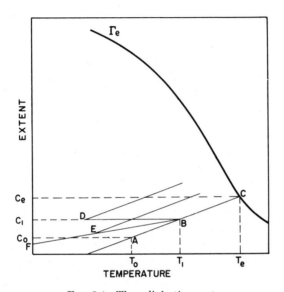

FIG. 3.1. The adiabatic reactor.

holding between temperature and extent in any one adiabatic bed, is a line such as ABC. Along it the rate of reaction is given by

$$R(c;c_0,T_0) = r(c,T_0 + H\overline{c - c_0}). \tag{9}$$

This has a maximum where

$$\frac{\partial r}{\partial c} + H \frac{\partial r}{\partial T} = 0, \tag{10}$$

and falls again to zero at the point C, where AB intersects $\Gamma_e$. In the neighborhood of C the reaction rate is slow and a bed length proportional to its logarithm is needed to achieve a small change in $c$.

Suppose that it proves desirable to stop the reaction at B and cool before reacting in another bed. If interchanger cooling is used, the state will lie on the line BD after cooling, for there will be no change in the extent of reaction. If however the cooling is accomplished by mixing with a cold feed, represented by the point F say, then the resulting state will lie on the line BEF. In the next bed the reaction path is represented by a line of slope $H$ through D or E. In general terms we may expect the line segments representing the reaction in the beds (such as AB) to lie in the neighborhood of the curve of maximum reaction rate defined by Eq. (10). It can be seen that with interchanger cooling any degree of conversion can be attained by a sufficient number of sufficiently long beds. With cold shot cooling however, the greatest extent that can possibly be attained is the equilibrium extent for adiabatic reaction from the cold shot state (F). It is the relative simplicity of the cold shot cooling that makes it attractive when only small conversions are needed.

## 3.4. The Tubular Reactor

Though in later applications we may return to the concentration unit of moles per unit volume, let us take the opportunity, in discussing the tubular reactor, to use the unit of moles per unit mass. In this we follow Amundson (1958), whose work has done so much to set chemical reactor design on a sound analytical basis. We shall still assume that the flow is uniform and that there is no longitudinal diffusion. Thus $G$, the flow rate in mass per unit area per unit time, is constant throughout the reactor under all circumstances. The linear velocity $v$ and the density $\rho$ may vary, but their product is constant, $\rho v = G$. Then a mass balance of $A_i$ over an element of length yields the differential equation

$$G \frac{dg_i}{dx} = \frac{d}{dx} (vc_i) = \sum \alpha_{ij} r^j, \tag{1}$$

where $r^j$ may be expressed as functions of $g_1, \ldots g_n, \rho, p, T$. By the relations (3.1.4) we can make the $r^j$ functions of extents $g^1, \ldots g^m$ and the reference composition $g_{i0}$, and using the independence of the reactions we obtain

$$G \frac{dg^j}{dx} = \frac{d}{dx} (vc^j) = r^j. \tag{2}$$

To derive the energy balance we define

44

$P$ = area of cooling surface per unit length

$T_c$ = temperature of coolant

$Q^*(T,T_c)$ = rate of heat removal per unit area of cooling surface

$J$ = mechanical equivalent of heat

$z(x)$ = height of the point above a datum.

Then the change in total energy (enthalpy + kinetic + potential) is equated to the heat added and the work done on an element to give

$$G \frac{d}{dx} \left\{ \sum_1^n g_i H_i(T) + \frac{v^2}{2J} + \frac{z}{J} \right\} + PQ^* = 0.$$

This equation can be rearranged by making use of (2) and (3.1.15), and by the definition of the specific heat of the mixture,

$$c_p = \sum_1^n g_i c_{pi} = \sum_1^n g_i (\partial H_i / \partial T), \tag{3}$$

to give

$$G c_p \frac{dT}{dx} + \frac{Gv}{J} \frac{dv}{dx} = -\frac{G}{J} \frac{dz}{dx} + \sum_1^m (-\Delta H_j) r^j - PQ^*. \tag{4}$$

The term $dz/dx$ is a known function of the position and geometry of the reactor and is probably negligible.

A momentum balance yields the equation

$$\frac{dp}{dx} + G \frac{dv}{dx} + \frac{\mathfrak{F}}{A} = 0 \tag{5}$$

where $\mathfrak{F}$ is the resistance to flow due to the packing and the tube. It is a function of $\rho$, $v$, and the nature of the packing.

If the cooling is by countercurrent or concurrent flow of a fluid stream, the temperature $T_c$ of the cooling stream will be governed by the equation

$$G_c A_c c_{pc} \frac{dT_c}{dx} = \pm PQ^*(T,T_c) \tag{6}$$

where

$G_c$ = flow rate of coolant (mass per unit area per unit time)

$A_c$ = cross-sectional area of coolant flow

$c_{pc}$ = specific heat of coolant,

and the positive and negative signs apply to concurrent and countercurrent cooling respectively.

45

Finally, we have an equation of the state

$$p = p(\rho, T) \tag{7}$$

and the identity

$$\rho v = G. \tag{8}$$

This makes up a set of $(m + 5)$ equations for $g^1, \ldots g^m$, $p$, $\rho$, $v$, $T$, and $T_c$, in the most general situation. If the coolant temperature can be prescribed, Eq. (6) is unnecessary; in fact, for reasons given below, we shall only discuss problems in which it is possible to choose $Q^*$ at each point, within certain limits.

If the kinetic and potential energies are ignored, Eqs. (2) and (4) become

$$G \frac{dg^j}{dx} = r^j \tag{9}$$

$$Gc_p \frac{dT}{dx} = \sum_1^m (-\Delta H_j)r^j - Q' \tag{10}$$

and if $\rho$ is not present in the reaction rates $r^j$, these are complete in themselves, and Eqs. (5), (7), and (8) can later be used to get $v$, $p$, and $\rho$ if they are wanted. If however $\rho$ is important, then (2) and (4) must be solved simultaneously with (5), (7), and (8).

In case the density, and therefore the velocity, of the reactants is constant, the equations may be written

$$G \frac{dg^j}{dx} = v \frac{dc^j}{dx} = \frac{dc^j}{dt} = r^j \tag{11}$$

$$\frac{G}{\rho} \frac{dT}{dx} = v \frac{dT}{dx} = \frac{dT}{dt} = \sum_1^m H^j r^j - \frac{Q'}{C_p} \tag{12}$$

where $H^j = (-\Delta H_j)/C_p$ and $C_p = \rho c_p$. It will be seen that these are the equations taken for the adiabatic beds in the previous paragraph, save that there $Q'$ was of course zero.

It might be remarked here that in our applications $x$ will be measured from the end of the tubular reactor, in accordance with the convention of Section 2.4. This simply means that the sign of $x$ or $t$ is changed and we would write

$$\frac{dc^j}{dt} = -r^j, \qquad j = 1, \ldots m \tag{13}$$

$$\frac{dT}{dt} = -\sum_1^m H^j r^j + Q \tag{14}$$

where $Q = Q'/C_p = Q*P/C_p$. In this case, if the total holding time of the process is $\theta$, the inlet values that must be specified are $c^j(\theta)$, $j = 1, \ldots m$, and $T(\theta)$.

## 3.5. The Stirred Tank Sequence as a Model for the Tubular Reactor

If we take Eq. (3.2.9) and write it

$$\frac{c_{r+1}^j - c_r^j}{\theta_r} = -r^j \tag{1}$$

it is evident that as $\theta_r \to 0$ the equation becomes

$$\frac{dc^j}{dt} = -r^j, \tag{2}$$

namely (3.4.13), the equation for a tubular reactor with $t$ the continuous variable reckoned from the end. Thus the tubular reactor is, as we should expect, the limit of an infinite number of infinitesimal stirred tanks. However, Amundson, Coste, and Rudd (1961) have shown that a much more interesting model arises if we take a large number of small stirred tanks, for it appears that by correctly choosing the size of these we can construct a model for the tubular reactor with longitudinal diffusion. Let us see how this is done in the simplest case.

Consider a sequence of identical stirred tank reactors, all at the same temperature, in which a first order irreversible reaction A $\to$ B takes place. If the feed concentration of A is 1 and the extent of reaction $c^1$, the concentration of A at any time is $c = 1 - c^1$; we will take this as the concentration variable. Then

$$r^j = kc_r$$

and

$$c_{r+1} = c_r(1 + k\theta) \tag{3}$$

where $\theta$ is the common holding time of the tanks. If there are $R$ stages in the sequence, the concentration of A in the product stream is

$$c_1 = (1 + k\theta)^{-R} \tag{4}$$

since $c_{R+1} = 1$.

Now if we consider the idealized tubular reactor with uniform

47

flow but with a longitudinal diffusion expressible by means of an apparent diffusion coefficient $D$, we arrive at the equation

$$D \frac{d^2c}{dx^2} + v \frac{dc}{dx} - kc = 0. \tag{5}$$

If the total length of the reactor is $L$, Eq. (5) should be solved subject to the conditions

$$\frac{D}{v} \frac{dc}{dx} + c = 1 \quad \text{at} \quad x = L$$

$$\frac{dc}{dx} = 0 \quad \text{at} \quad x = 0.$$

However, if we assume that $L$ is very large compared with $D/v$, these conditions simplify and we may solve (5) subject to $c = 1$ at $x = L$ and $c$ becomes small as $x \to 0$. Then the solution is

$$c = \exp\left[-m(L - x)\right], \tag{6}$$

where $m$ is the positive root of

$$Dm^2 + vm - k = 0. \tag{7}$$

Thus at the end $x = 0$

$$c(0) = \exp\left[-mL\right]. \tag{8}$$

Suppose that the length $L$ of the tubular reactor is equivalent to $R$ small stirred tanks; for the total holding times to be the same, $L = R\theta v$. If the exit concentrations are to be the same, then, by (4) and (8),

$$(1 + k\theta)^{-R} = \exp\left[-mv\theta R\right]$$

or

$$mv\theta = \log\left(1 + k\theta\right) \tag{9}$$

Let

$$\varpi = \frac{v^2\theta}{2D} \quad \text{and} \quad \delta = \frac{2kD}{v^2}; \tag{10}$$

$\varpi$ is a Peclet number based on the length of tubular reactor, $v\theta/2$, that corresponds to one half of the stirred tank. Then by Eq. (7)

$$mv\theta = \varpi\{\sqrt{1 + 2\delta} - 1\}$$

and

$$k\theta = \varpi\delta$$

Thus (9) is an equation for $\varpi$ in terms of $\delta$:

$$\varpi\{\sqrt{1 + 2\delta} - 1\} = \log\left(1 + \varpi\delta\right) \tag{11}$$

48

and given the diffusion coefficient $D$ the corresponding size of stirred tank $\theta$ can be found that will exactly model the tubular reactor for this particular reaction. The relation between $\varpi$ and $\delta$ is shown in Fig. 3.2. For low reaction rates $\varpi$ is quite close to 1, which corre-

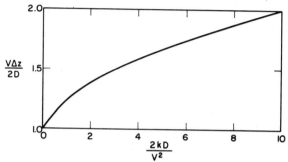

FIG. 3.2. Size of the stirred tank in the model for a tubular reactor with diffusion.

sponds to the model of a packed bed proposed by Amundson and Aris (1957).

It is of course a much more hazardous thing to assume that the model will be adequate in more general situations. Two arguments may be advanced as grounds for justifying an investigation of the analogy. First, we may point out that in a packed bed the so-called longitudinal diffusion is really a matter of streams splitting and recombining around particles and mixing in the interstices. Even the effect of lateral diffusion with flow variations has been shown by Taylor (1954) to be equivalent to an apparent longitudinal diffusion. If then the mechanism of diffusion is a hydrodynamic one, it will result in all the species and the temperature having the same diffusion coefficient. This is clearly necessary if the model is to have any chance of succeeding. Secondly, we may regard $c_r^j$ as a function of a continuous variable $x = r\theta/v$, and expand $c_{r+1}^j$ in Eq. (1) by a Taylor's series. Then

$$\frac{v^2\theta}{2}\frac{d^2c^j}{dx^2} + v\frac{dc^j}{dx} + r^j = O(\theta^2).$$

By keeping $\theta$ finite but neglecting terms of order $\theta^2$, we have

$$D\frac{d^2c^j}{dx^2} + v\frac{dc^j}{dx} + r^j = 0 \tag{12}$$

if $D = v^2\theta/2$. But this last equation is the equation for the tubular

49

reactor with diffusion, and the choice of $\theta$ corresponds to making the Peclet number $\varpi = 1$.

How much more successful the model is than could have been hoped has been demonstrated by Amundson, Coste, and Rudd (1959). They have compared the solutions of Eqs. (1) and (12) and their associated equations for temperature in considerable detail. This is not easy, for there are two boundary conditions on (12), one at the inlet $x = L$ and the other at the outlet $x = 0$. Thus to integrate (12) numerically it is necessary to guess the derivative at $x = L$ and integrate towards $x = 0$. If this does not lead to the satisfaction of the condition at $x = 0$, another guess is made at the initial derivative. Unfortunately this process is doomed to complete frustration, for however accurate the guess the solution blows up a short way down the reactor. But if the stirred tank model with $\varpi = 1$ is used, the feed conditions are known exactly and Eqs. (3.2.9) and (3.2.10) can be solved without guesswork. By way of confirmation, Eq. (12) and the associated temperature equation were integrated from $x = 0$ to $x = L$ using as starting values the functional and derivative values obtained from the stirred tank model. In this di-

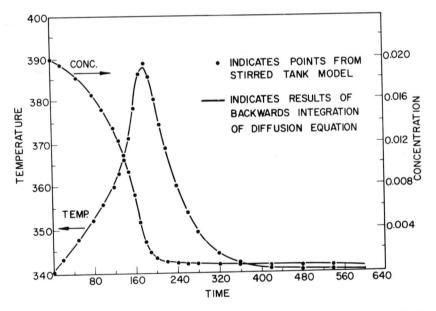

FIG. 3.3. Comparison of concentration and temperature profiles for a tubular reactor and sequence of stirred tanks. (Courtesy of N. R. Amundson.)

50

rection the numerical integration is stable and the integration confirms the model to an amazing degree of accuracy. A typical result is shown in Fig. 3.3, where the excellent confirmation of the backward integration and instability of the forward integration are evident.

This gives us considerable confidence in this model and shows the importance of considering the optimal design of a sequence of identical stirred tank reactors.

## 3.6. *The Batch Reactor*

In the batch reactor, given quantities of the reactants are put into a vessel and allowed to react. A cooling or heating coil and a means of stirring may be provided, and the course of the reaction is controlled by heating or cooling and by the length of time the reaction is allowed to proceed. The tendency in modern chemical engineering has been to move away from batch processes and to use continuous flow reactors. Where it is still used, the batch process is one unit in a chain of operations which follow a regular time cycle. The economics of this operation will depend to a large extent on the work needed to recharge the reactor. There is a formal similarity between the time from the beginning of a batch reaction and the holding time from the inlet to a tubular reactor, and precisely the same equations are obtained by mass and energy balances over an elementary interval as were obtained in Section 3.4. It should be noted however that the rate of heat removal $Q$ is far more flexible in the batch reactor, for it is easy to change the flow rate of coolant with time or even bring an auxiliary cooling coil into action, whereas a tubular reactor cannot accommodate drastic variations in interchanger design within its length.

The formal similarity allows us to carry over the equations for mass and energy balances in the tubular reactor, Eqs. (3.4.11)–(3.4.14). The momentum equation has no meaning. Care must be taken however to distinguish between a batch reactor working at constant volume and one that works at constant pressure. The latter has the Eqs. (3.4.12) or (3.4.14) which were derived from an enthalpy balance. In the former case the heat added would be equated to the internal energy change. Thus in this case $c_v$ should replace $c_p$ and the internal energy of reaction replace the heat of reaction. These

51

changes involve only a reinterpretation of $H^j$ and $Q$, so that we may allow the equations to stand as they are. In applications we will use them in the form

$$\frac{dc^j}{dt} = -r^j \qquad\qquad j = 1, \ldots m \qquad (1)$$

$$\frac{dT}{dt} = -\sum_1^m H^j r^j + Q \qquad\qquad (2)$$

where $Q$ is proportional to the rate of heat removal and $t$ is the time from the end of the process.

## 3.7. Cooling

A brief discussion of the rate of heat removal is in order, as it will justify an expression that we need later. It will be assumed that the heat is removed by means of an interchanger, probably in the form of a tube through which a coolant flows. If the local temperature of the reactants is $T$ and that of the coolants is $T_c$, the rate of heat transfer per unit area is expressed in the form $k(T - T_c)$. The reciprocal of $k$, the resistance to heat transfer, is the sum of three terms. The first is the resistance on the reactant side, which will be a function of the reactant properties and state of flow. The second is the resistance of the tube wall; this is usually quite small. The third is the resistance on the coolant side, which will depend on the properties and flow of the coolant and size of the tube. A popular correlation makes this last resistance proportional to $(d/U^4)^{1/5}$, where $d$ is the diameter of the tube and $U$ the linear velocity of the coolant.

If a stirred tank reactor of temperature $T$ is cooled by a coil of tube of length $l$ and diameter $d$, the heat removal can be calculated as follows. Over a length $\Delta x$ at a distance $x$ from the inlet, the amount of heat transferred in unit time is

$$\Delta Q = k(T - T_c)\pi d \, \Delta x$$

where $T_c$ is the temperature of the coolant at $x$. This raises the temperature of the coolant by $\Delta T_c$, where

$$\Delta Q = U\pi d^2 \rho_c c_{pc} \Delta T_c / 4$$

$\rho_c$ and $c_{pc}$ being the density and specific heat of the coolant. In the limit we have

52

$$\frac{dQ}{dx} = \frac{U\pi d^2 \rho_c c_{pc} d}{4} \frac{T_c}{dx} = k\pi d(T - T_c).$$ (1)

If the coolant enters at temperature $T_{c1}$ and leaves at $T_{c2}$, then

$$\ln \frac{T - T_{c1}}{T - T_{c2}} = \frac{4kl}{dU\rho_c c_{pc}} = \kappa.$$ (2)

The total rate of heat removal is

$$Q = k(\pi dl)(T - T_{c1}) \frac{1 - e^{-\kappa}}{\kappa},$$ (3)

which is a fraction $(1 - e^{-\kappa})/\kappa$ of what it would be if the coolant were always at temperature $T_{c1}$.

# 4 The Objective Function

*"Come, listen, my men, while I tell you again*
*The five unmistakable marks*
*By which you may know, wheresoever you go,*
*The warranted genuine Snarks."*

IT WAS REMARKED in the introduction that we are forced to consider problems which are rather less ambitious than we would like, and that we have, for this reason, restricted ourselves to the reactor as the unit of study. We must now sketch the various objective functions we shall take up and see how they relate to the optimum problem. In the following description, it is not intended to divide the objective functions into entirely separate classes but to show how they may be built up to a reasonably realistic standard. The simpler are often special cases of the more general, but they also have an interest in themselves.

## 4.1. Stoichiometric Objective Functions

By a stoichiometric objective function we mean one which is concerned only with the changes in concentration of the species. Thus, if for the moment we define $c_{if}$ and $c_{ip}$ to be the concentrations of $A_i$ in the feed and product streams, such an objective function is of the form

$$P(c_{1p} - c_{1f}, \ldots, c_{np} - c_{nf}). \tag{1}$$

In the simplest case we seek to maximize the production of a particular species, say $A_1$. If $q$ is the flow rate through the reactor, then the net rate of production of $A_1$ is $q(c_{1p} - c_{1f})$. Now $q$ is on rather a different basis from the operating variables for it cannot be altered from stage to stage. If there is any need to find the optimal value of $q$ for a multistage process we must first find the optimal policy for a given $q$ and the consequent maximum of the objective function. The process of optimization is then repeated until the $q$ that gives the greatest maximum is found. Fortunately however this is not always necessary with a stoichiometric objective function, for it will be recalled that the equations for the various types of reactors involve only the holding time of the process. (An exception is the full set of equations for the tubular reactor.) This is the ratio of the volume of a stage to the flow rate $q$, so that when the optimal policy for holding times is known the optimal policy for volumes is also known for any value of $q$. It follows that if we take $(c_{1p} - c_{1f})$ as the objective function and maximize this, we shall have the optimal policy for the greatest production of $A_1$. If the production of $A_1$ is to be fixed at a certain level, this policy then gives us the minimum flow rate that will attain this production.

Another example of a stoichiometric function would arise if we wished to maximize the production of one species, say $A_1$, relative to the usage of another, say $A_2$. In this case we would set

$$P = (c_{1p} - c_{1f})/(c_{2f} - c_{2p}). \tag{2}$$

An alternative way of doing this would be by use of a Lagrange multiplier. If we take

$$P = (c_{1p} - c_{1f}) + \mu(c_{2p} - c_{2f}) \tag{3}$$

and maximize this, the resulting ratio (2) will be a function of $\mu$, and we seek the $\mu$ that will maximize this ratio.

## 4.2. Material Objective Functions

By a material objective function we mean one that is concerned with the increase in value of the process stream. If the component species can be mixed or separated at negligible cost we may write the increase in value of the stream as

$$P = \sum_1^n v_i(c_{ip} - c_{if}) \tag{1}$$

where $v_i$ is the value of a unit amount of $A_i$. This may be expressed in terms of the difference in extent of reaction in product and feed (denoted by $c_p^j$ and $c_f^j$ respectively) for

$$c_{ip} - c_{if} = \sum_{j=1}^{m} \alpha_{ij}(c_p^j - c_f^j) \tag{2}$$

Thus

$$P = \sum_{1}^{m} V_j(c_p^j - c_f^j) \tag{3}$$

where

$$V_j = \sum_{i=1}^{n} v_i\alpha_{ij}$$

is the increase in value due to a unit increase in extent of the $j$th reaction. The main reaction for which the process was designed will have a positive value, but there may be undesirable side reactions. If the products of these are given zero or negative values, the corresponding $V_j$ will be negative with our sign convention for stoichiometric coefficients.

It is not always possible to regard the species in the mixture as having independent values. The cost of separating them or removing one or two may well be a nonlinear function of their concentrations. Thus as a general material objective function we would take

$$P = v(c_{1p}, \ldots c_{np})$$

or

$$P = v(c_{1p}, \ldots c_{np}) - v(c_{1f}, \ldots c_{nf}), \tag{4}$$

with $v$ some piecewise continuous and differentiable function. Into such a function we could build a lot of realistic information. If for example the product had to fulfill a certain specification

$$c_{n*} \leq c_{np} \leq c_n^*,$$

we might set $v \equiv 0$ for $c_n$ outside this range. This is particularly useful for keeping the undesirable by-products below certain tolerance levels.

If the product of the reactor goes to a separating unit such as extractor or distillation column, we may take $v$ to be the value of the product after separation minus the costs of separation. If an optimal policy is used for the separating unit, then the principle of optimality shows that the optimal policy using this objective function will give the optimal design for the reactor and separating unit as a whole.

## 4.3. Objective Functions with Operating Costs

To construct a more realistic objective function we retain the general material objective function and subtract from it the important operating costs. Of these we can here only speak in general, for much of the detail is of a special nature, perhaps even private to a particular company. What sort of detail may be involved is indicated in the next paragraph.

The operating costs may be roughly broken down under four heads.

### (1) *Capital and Maintenance Charges*

The capital cost of a reactor is a function of the number of stages, their complexity and operating conditions, and of the flow rate and properties of the reactant stream. This cost has to be financed and repaid over a certain period of years from the profit of the plant. Experience gives some idea of the kind of maintenance that is needed with various kinds of reactors and what fraction of the year they are liable to be out of production. All these factors must be considered, together with the estimated useful life of the plant and current economic predictions, in order to arrive at a number $C_1$, the combined cost per unit time of these charges.

### (2) *Stream Costs*

By this we mean the cost of maintaining the flow of the process stream and the pressures of the system. These costs will depend on the flow rate and required pressures and also, in a less predictable way, on the layout of the plant. Normally certain general principles of layout and design are followed, and these would be assumed in estimating the costs. In matters of detail, such as pipe diameter or intermediate compression stages, the optimal policy is often quite accurately known and should be used. All this can be reduced to a single figure $C_2$, the cost per unit time of maintaining the stream.

### (3) *Heat Costs*

In this we include the costs of heating or cooling the process stream and of adding or removing heat from the reactors. The costs of insulation and capital cost of interchangers would be included

58

in $C_1$, but the cost of supplying fuel to a furnace or cooling water to an interchanger belong here. The heat costs per unit time, $C_3$, will be a function primarily of the flow rate and operating temperatures.

## (4) Control Costs

The amount of instrumentation and supervision that a reactor needs is much more difficult to estimate. It will be a function of the number and complexity of the stages but may also require the consideration of the natural stability of the required steady state. The optimal policy not including the control cost might specify an unstable mode of operation, and the cost of control might be so great as to give a vastly different optimal policy when included. This item, $C_4$, also includes the wages of the workers supervising the running of the plant.

The costs can now be combined to give a grand objective function. If $\lambda$ is the fraction of the year that the reactor is in operation (a factor that has been included in the cost estimates $C_i$) the net profit per unit time is

$$P = \lambda q \{v(c_p) - v(c_f)\} - \{C_1 + C_2 + C_3 + C_4\}. \qquad (1)$$

In the detailed costing one general principle can be asserted: Any item working between two fixed conditions should be designed to do so at minimum cost.

## 4.4. An Example of Cost Estimation

To show something of the detail that has to be gone into in estimating these costs, we will look at the example considered by Westbrook (1960). A single stirred tank reactor is to be considered, with reactants whose physical properties are like those of benzene. $q$ is the flow rate in gallons per hour and $T$ the temperature in °F, and the construction cost is required in terms of these.

If $\theta$ is the holding time in hours, the volume of the reactor is

$$V = q\theta \text{ gallons} = 0.1337q\theta \text{ ft}^3. \qquad (1)$$

The reactor consists of a cylindrical shell of length 1.75 times its diameter capped by semiellipsoidal ends. There is also an allowance of 5 per cent extra volume for an external heat exchanger. Thus if $d$ is the diameter of the cylinder in feet,

$$V = 1.70d^3 \text{ ft}^3. \qquad (2)$$

The diameter must lie within the limits

$$1.25 < d < 9.67, \tag{3}$$

and if $d$ exceeds the upper limit the process must be divided into parallel units. To estimate the cost of supporting the vessel, the vessel is assumed to be elevated 10 ft above grade and supported by a skirt of the same diameter and thickness. This is of course not an accurate design of the supporting structure but it does make some allowance for the size and weight of the vessel.

To keep the reactants liquid, the reactor must operate at a pressure above their vapor pressure, which is given by

$$p = 1.15 \times 10^6 \times 10^{-3120/(T+460)} \text{ psi.}$$

However, a much more convenient expression and one which fits the data well is

$$p = 3.3 \times 10^{-6} T^3 \text{ psi.} \tag{4}$$

In pressure vessel design a minimum of 50 psi, and a design pressure 25 psi greater than the operating pressure, are used. Thus the design pressure of the reaction vessel is

$$p_d = \begin{cases} 50 \text{ psi} & T \leq 200 \text{ °F} \\ 25 + 3.3 \times 10^{-6} T^3 \text{ psi} & T > 200 \text{ °F.} \end{cases} \tag{5}$$

The cost of pressure vessel construction can be estimated in terms of its weight. To find this we need to calculate the thickness which is given by

$$t = p_d d/2s + 0.0104 \text{ ft} \tag{6}$$

for the cylindrical walls and

$$t = p_d d/4s + 0.0104 \text{ ft} \tag{7}$$

for the ends. Here $s$ is the allowable working stress, which below 500 °F can be taken to be 16,000 psi with small error. The 0.0104 ft = 1/8 in. is a corrosion allowance.

Finally, the areas involved are $4.70d^2$ ft$^2$ for the cylinder and $2.46d^2$ ft$^2$ for the ends. Combining all these items we arrive at an expression for the total weight

$$W = (0.0909d^3 + 0.432d^2)p_d + 36.6d^2 + 160.5d \text{ lb.} \tag{8}$$

The cost of steel vessel construction has been correlated with this weight and, according to estimated 1959 costs, was given by

$$C_r = 3.5W^{0.782} \text{ \$.} \tag{9}$$

## 4.4. AN EXAMPLE OF COST ESTIMATION

We thus arrive at a construction cost for the vessel as a function of $d$ and $T$, namely,

$$C_r = \begin{cases} 3.5[4.56d^3 + 60.7d^2 + 160.5d]^{0.782}, & T \leq 200 \text{ °F} \\ 3.5[(.0909d^3 + 0.432d^2)(25 + 3.3 \times 10^{-6}T^3) \\ \qquad + 36.6d^2 + 160.5d]^{0.782}, & T > 200 \text{ °F}. \end{cases} \tag{10}$$

To this must be added a cost for insulation which by a similar analysis is estimated at

$$C_i = \begin{cases} 0 & T \leq 200 \text{ °F} \\ (17.1 + 1.33 \times 10^{-2}T)d^2 & T > 200 \text{ °F}. \end{cases} \tag{11}$$

Finally, there are miscellaneous costs such as the provision of a ladder, platform, and an adequate foundation. These proved to be expressible in the form

$$C_m = 1000 + 100d \text{ \$}. \tag{12}$$

The stirring requirements for average mixing duty are estimated at 5 hp per 100 ft$^3$, and combining this with the cost data on mixer-motor installations gives

$$C_s = 255V^{0.3} \text{ \$}. \tag{13}$$

Thus an estimate of the reactor cost, $C_r + C_i + C_m + C_s$, excluding the external heat exchanger, can be obtained for any given $V$ and $T$ by combining Eqs. (10)–(13). All this requires a good deal of searching through the trade literature and estimating increases in costs from the latest available data. It falls outside the proper scope of the present volume to treat this in any greater detail, but it is a necessary part of constructing the proposed objective functions. An analysis of this kind needs patience and shrewdness such as displayed in the reference from which this section has been abstracted. Even though it results in very cumbersome expressions these present little difficulty to the digital computer and problems of an appalling complexity can be successfully handled.

## 4.5. The Relation of the Objective Function to the Optimal Problem

It has been emphasized that the classes of objective function that have been outlined are by no means watertight; however, provided they are not held to too rigidly they give a useful classification of optimal problems. In the following chapters we shall take up the study of different types of reactors and build up a sequence of useful cases which will show the particular features of the reactor system and lead to a discussion of general problems. It should be remembered however that the methods used for one particular reaction-reactor system and objective function are not necessarily suitable for another. At every turn there is scope for all the ingenuity and acumen the optimizer can muster.

In general, the optimal policy for an $R$-stage process does not require optimal single-stage conditions in each stage. The principle of optimality only asserts that every coterminous $r$-stage policy should be optimal, $r \leq R$. An optimal policy for which each stage uses some part of the optimal single stage policy will be called disjoint with respect to that part of the policy. This disjunction depends on the objective function used and may be destroyed by a more complete objective function. The only case of partial disjunction that has been found is that of a single reaction with a linear (or monotonic) material objective function.

We have generally used the direct construction of an objective function as some measure of the profit. This then has to be maximized. An important form of problem is to take the objective function as a measure of the cost and to minimize it. In some cases the same problem can be formulated in two ways which are duals of one another. Thus, if we seek the minimum holding time to achieve a given conversion we are solving the dual of the problem of finding the maximum conversion for given holding time. The existence of duality is useful but it needs to be carefully established, as, for example, in Amundson and Bilous (1956).

# 5

# The Continuous Flow Stirred Tank Reactor

*We have sailed many weeks, we have sailed many days*
  *(Seven days to the week I allow),*
*But a Snark, on the which we might lovingly gaze,*
  *We have never beheld till now!*

In this chapter we shall consider the problems associated with a sequence of stirred tank reactors. The optimal policy involves the choice of the holding time and temperature of each stage in such a way that the final conversion is as profitable as possible. We might also have considered pressure as an operating variable to be chosen at each stage, but in cases where this is important the reader will have no difficulty in seeing how it could be accommodated. In very many cases the temperature is the most important variable and the optimum is relatively insensitive to changes in holding time. We shall first show the disjoint character of the optimal temperature policy when only one reaction is taking place. This may be used to simplify the discussion of all problems with a single reaction. Following this, mention will be made of two consecutive reactions and of the system of four reactions first propounded by Denbigh, before the general method of solution is given. Finally, some consideration will be given to the problem in which some of the feed is bypassed to later reactors.

63

## 5.1. *The Disjoint Character of the Optimal Temperature Policy with a Single Reaction*

We wish first of all to show that when only one reaction is taking place the temperature should always be chosen so that the rate of reaction will be as large as possible. This has long been known from experience or assumed by "common sense," but in fact it requires mathematical proof, which is not difficult to produce.

We have seen in Chapter 3 that if $c_i$ is the concentration of the chemical species $A_i$ which is taking part in the reaction $\sum_1^n \alpha_i A_i = 0$, then $c_i = c_{i0} + \alpha_i c$, where $c_{i0}$ is the concentration in some reference state and $c$ the extent of reaction. The rate of reaction, $r(c,T)$, is defined as the time derivative of $c$ and is a function of $c$ and the temperature $T$. (We are assuming that the pressure and reference composition are constant.) The sequence of $R$ reactors is numbered from the last to the first (see Fig. 5.1) and a suffix $r$ denotes values

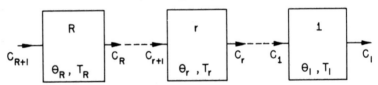

Fig. 5.1. The stirred tank sequence.

appropriate to reactor $r$, the $r$th from the end. Then, as in Section 3.2, we have the equations

$$c_{r+1} = c_r - \theta_r r(c_r, T_r), \quad r = 1, \ldots R, \qquad (1)$$

where $\theta_r$ is the holding time of reactor $r$. There will normally be certain restrictions on the temperature of the form

$$T_* \leq T_r \leq T^*. \qquad (2)$$

The objective function to be considered is of one of the simpler types, either stoichiometric or material. In the first case it is required to maximize the final extent of reaction, $c_1$; in the second case this will also be required if the objective function is monotonically increasing with $c_1$. Here the interesting problem is to find the optimal policy subject to some restriction on the total holding time, say

$$\sum_1^R \theta_r = \Theta, \doteq \Theta_R \qquad (3)$$

for otherwise, equilibrium at the most favorable temperature can be approached as closely as is desired by use of an exceedingly long holding time in the final reactor. If there is some reason for aiming at a particular extent of reaction in the product, then the problem might be to achieve this with the least total holding time. It will appear that the two problems are equivalent.

Let us consider first the choice of temperature and holding time such that a given conversion, $c_1$, is achieved from a given feed state, $c_{R+1}$, in the least total holding time. This total holding time will be

$$\Theta_R = \sum_1^R \theta_r = \sum_1^R \frac{c_r - c_{r+1}}{r(c_r, T_r)} \qquad (4)$$

and the optimal policy involves the choice of $(2R - 1)$ quantities, $T_1, \ldots T_R, \theta_2, \ldots \theta_R$. $\theta_1$ cannot be chosen arbitrarily but must be such that the required conversion $c_1$ is achieved. When these choices have been made we see that the value of $\Theta_R$ depends only on $c_{R+1}$, the feed state. Let

$$f_R(c_{R+1}) = \text{Min } \Theta_R. \qquad (5)$$

Then, by the principle of optimality,

$$f_R(c_{R+1}) = \text{Min} \left\{ \frac{c_R - c_{R+1}}{r(c_R, T_R)} + f_{R-1}(c_R) \right\}, \qquad (6)$$

where the minimum is to be attained by correct choice of $\theta_R$ and $T_R$ or, equivalently, by choice of $c_R$ and $T_R$. We see immediately that as far as the choice of $T_R$ is concerned it should always be such that $r(c_R, T_R)$ is as large as possible, for $T_R$ enters into only the first term. Thus at every stage $T_R$ should be chosen so that for the state $c_R$ of that stage the rate of reaction is as large as possible. Let us denote this maximum value by $R(c_R)$. Then

$$f_R(c_{R+1}) = \text{Min} \left\{ \frac{c_R - c_{R+1}}{R(c_R)} + f_{R-1}(c_R) \right\}, \qquad (7)$$

and the minimization involves only the choice of $c_R$. We shall return to this problem later.

Two formulations of the problem of maximizing $c_1$ subject to the restriction (3) are possible. In the first we recognize that the maximum value of $c_1$ will depend on the feed state $c_{R+1}$ and the total available holding time. Let

$$g_R(c_{R+1}, \Theta) = \text{Max } (c_1 - c_{R+1}). \qquad (8)$$

65

Then, writing

$$c_1 - c_{R+1} = \sum_1^R (c_r - c_{r+1})$$

and applying the principle of optimality,

$$g_R(c_{R+1}, \Theta) = \text{Max} \{ c_R - c_{R+1} + g_{R-1}(c_R, \Theta - \theta_R) \}$$
$$= \text{Max} \{ \theta_R r(c_R, T_R) + g_{R-1}(c_R, \Theta - \theta_R) \}. \qquad (9)$$

The maximization here involves the correct choice of $\theta_R$ and $T_R$, and $T_R$ should evidently be chosen to maximize the reaction rate. The second formulation involves the use of the Lagrange multiplier, and we seek the maximum of

$$(c_1 - c_{R+1}) - \lambda \Theta_R = \sum_1^R \{ c_r - c_{r+1} - \lambda \theta_r \}$$

unrestricted by the condition (3). Let

$$g_{R,\lambda}(c_{R+1}) = \text{Max} \sum_1^R \{ c_r - c_{r+1} - \lambda \theta_r \}$$

$$= \text{Max} \sum_1^R (c_r - c_{r+1}) \left\{ 1 - \frac{\lambda}{r(c_r, T_r)} \right\}, \qquad (10)$$

then, again using the principle of optimality,

$$g_{R,\lambda}(c_{R+1}) = \text{Max} \left[ (c_R - c_{R+1}) \left\{ 1 - \frac{\lambda}{r(c_R, T_R)} \right\} + g_{R-1,\lambda}(c_R) \right] \qquad (11)$$

and $T_R$ should be chosen to maximize $r(c_R, T_R)$. The resulting $\Theta_R$ will be a function of $\lambda$, and the condition (3) is satisfied by choosing the correct value of $\lambda$.

A formulation of the other problem by use of the Lagrange multiplier would be as follows. Let us seek the minimum of $\Theta_R - \mu(c_1 - c_{R+1})$ without restriction on the value of $c_1$. For given $\mu$ this minimum will be a function only of $c_{R+1}$ and we can write

$$h_{R,\mu}(c_{R+1}) = \text{Min} \sum_1^R \{ \theta_r - \mu(c_r - c_{r+1}) \}$$

$$= \text{Min} \sum_1^R (c_r - c_{r+1}) \left\{ \frac{1}{r(c_r, T_r)} - \mu \right\}. \qquad (12)$$

But now it is evident that

$$g_{R,\lambda}(c_{R+1}) = -\lambda h_{R,1/\lambda}(c_{R+1})$$

and so the two problems are equivalent.

A slightly more general problem with a disjoint temperature policy would be that in which the total cost is to be minimized when the cost of any stage depends on the holding time only. If this were a function of temperature also the policy would no longer be disjoint.

## 5.2. *The Sequence of Reactors of Equal Size*

Although it does not now require the use of dynamic programming, it will be convenient to notice the especially simple case of reactors of equal (or prescribed) size. The importance of this special case lies in the fact that it is sometimes necessary to use identical reactors, and also in the value of such a sequence as a model of the tubular reactor with diffusion.

We will again let $R(c)$ denote the maximum value of $r(c,T)$, attained when $T = T_m(c)$, and require that

$$T_* \leq T_m \leq T^*.$$

It is worth noting that $R(c)$ can sometimes be obtained explicitly, and a case of particular value is that in which $r$ has a form commonly assumed for homogeneous reactions. This is

$$r(c,T) = k_1(T) \prod_1^n c_i^{\beta_i} - k_2(T) \prod_1^n c_i^{\gamma_i} \tag{1}$$

where $\beta_1, \ldots \beta_n$ and $\gamma_1, \ldots \gamma_n$ are exponents denoting the order of the forward and backward reactions with respect to each species. The $\beta_i$ and $\gamma_i$ are restricted by the relations $\gamma_i - \beta_i = \alpha_i$, which makes them consistent with the equilibrium relation $\prod_1^n c_i^{\alpha_i} = k_1/k_2 = K(T)$. $k_1$ and $k_2$ are functions of $T$ only and have the form

$$k_i = k_i \exp\left[-E_i/RT\right] \qquad i = 1,2. \tag{2}$$

Since we are looking for a maximum at constant $c$ all the $c_i$ will be constant, and if this maximum lies between $T_*$ and $T^*$ it will satisfy

$$\frac{\partial r}{\partial T} = \frac{1}{RT^2}\left(E_1 k_1 \prod_1^n c_i^{\beta_i} - E_2 k_2 \prod_1^n c_i^{\gamma_i}\right) = 0. \tag{3}$$

Now $r$ is positive, so that the first term in (1) is greater than the second. Consequently there is no hope of Eq. (3) being satisfied if $E_1 > E_2$, for then the first term in (3) would be even larger than the second and $\partial r/\partial T$ would be positive. The heat of reaction $\Delta H = E_1 - E_2$ is positive for endothermic reactions and so for such

67

reactions the maximum rate is always attained at the highest possible temperature, $T^*$. With an exothermic reaction, however, for which $(-\Delta H) = E_2 - E_1$ is positive, Eq. (3) can be solved for $T_m$, in the form

$$\frac{k_1(T_m)}{k_2(T_m)} = K(T_m) = \frac{E_2}{E_1} \prod_1^n c_i^{\alpha_i} \tag{4}$$

Because $E_2 > E_1$ and $K(T)$ is a decreasing function, Eq. 4 shows that $T_m < T_e$, the equilibrium temperature at which $K(T_e) = \prod_1^n c_i^{\alpha_i}$. Furthermore, we see that at this point $\partial^2 r / \partial T^2$ is proportional to

$$E_1^2 k_1 \prod_1^n c_i^{\beta_i} - E_2^2 k_2 \prod_1^n c_i^{\gamma_i}$$

and so is negative; thus the extremum is indeed a maximum. Explicitly, (4) gives

$$T_m(c) = \frac{(-\Delta H)}{R} \left[ \ln \frac{k_2^* E_2}{k_1^* E_1} \prod_1^n (c_{i0} + \alpha_i c)^{\alpha_i} \right]^{-1}. \tag{5}$$

If the value of $T_m$ given by (5) lies below $T_*$, then $T_m = T_*$; if it lies above $T^*$, then $T_m = T^*$. If

$$p = E_1/(E_2 - E_1), \tag{6}$$

then, when $T_m(c)$ lies in the range $(T_*, T^*)$, a little algebraic manipulation gives

$$R(c) = \frac{p^p}{(p+1)^{p+1}} \frac{k_1^{*p+1}}{k_2^{*p}} \prod_1^n (c_{i0} + \alpha_i c)^{\beta_i - p\alpha_i}. \tag{7}$$

When $T_m$ is outside this range we have $R(c) = r(c, T_*)$ or $R(c) = r(c, T^*)$.

It is not always possible to obtain an explicit form for $R(c)$ but it is always possible to calculate it either from a formula or from tables for $r(c, T)$. Since $\theta_r$ is prescribed, or $\theta_r = \theta$, Eq. (5.1.1) becomes an equation for $c_r$ in terms of $c_{r+1}$,

$$c_r - \theta R(c_r) = c_{r+1}. \tag{8}$$

This may be solved for $c_r$ as a function of the feed state $c_{r+1}$, say

$$c_r = \psi(c_{r+1}, \theta). \tag{9}$$

Then the best performance of this sequence of reactors can be found by repeatedly using this formula:

## 5.2. THE SEQUENCE OF REACTORS OF EQUAL SIZE

$$c_R = \psi(c_{R+1}, \theta_R)$$
$$c_{R-1} = \psi(c_R, \theta_{R-1}) \tag{10}$$
$$\cdot$$
$$\cdot$$
$$\cdot$$
$$c_1 = \psi(c_2, \theta_1).$$

The corresponding temperatures are $T_m(c_r)$, $r = 1, \ldots R$. Figure 5.2 shows a graphical construction for this iteration with three reactors

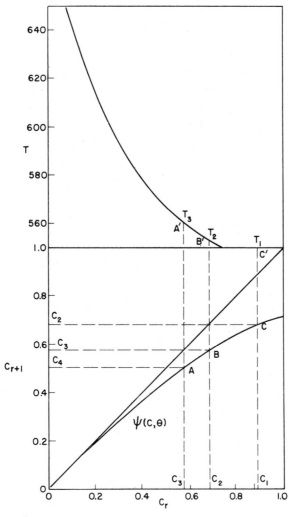

FIG. 5.2. Graphical construction for reactors of equal holding time.

of equal size. In the lower part of the figure the curve $\psi(c,\theta)$ is drawn. Starting from an ordinate $c_4$ we see that $c_3$ is the abscissa of the point A. The temperature in the reactor 3 is then given by $T_3$. Proceeding vertically from A to the line $c_r = c_{r+1}$ and across to B, we have $c_2$ as its ordinate and $T_2$ as the ordinate of the corresponding point B'. Another step gives the final product extent $c_1$ and the temperature $T_3$ of the last reactor.

Figures 5.2 and 5.3 are both based on calculations for a first-order

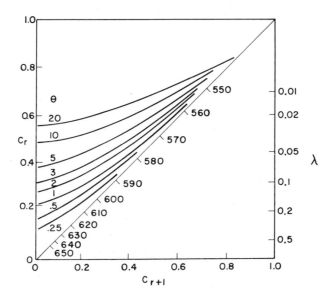

FIG. 5.3. Graphical construction for reactors of prescribed holding time.

reversible reaction $A_1 - A_2 = 0$. For this we may take $c_1 = c$ and $c_2 = 1 - c$ by taking $c_{10} + c_{20}$ to be the unit of concentration; for the calculations $\beta_1 = \gamma_2 = 0$, $\beta_2 = \gamma_1 = 1$ and values of $E_1 = 24{,}000$, $E_2 = 50{,}000$, $\ln k_1^* = 19$, $\ln k_2^* = 41$ were taken. The temperature was required to lie between 550 and 650 °K. Figure 5.3 shows how much more information may be put in a single diagram. In it a number of curves of $\psi$ are drawn for various $\theta$. Again one passes to and fro between the line $c_r = c_{r+1}$ and the appropriate curve in a zigzag of horizontal and vertical lines. It is not necessary to have a separate graph of $T_m$, for this can be put in as a scale on the line $c_r = c_{r+1}$ and immediately read off for any $c_r$. If the $\theta_r$ are prescribed

70

but not all equal, the appropriate $\theta$ curve should be used at each step.

If the cost of any stage is proportional to its holding time, we should look for the maximum of

$$c_1 - c_{R+1} - \lambda\Theta_R = \sum_1^R (c_r - c_{r+1} - \lambda\theta_r).$$

Now, clearly, it is no use adding a term to this sum if it has become negative, i.e., if $(c_r - c_{r+1})/\theta_r = R(c_r) < \lambda$. The scale of $\lambda$ or $R(c_r)$ on Fig. 5.3 shows where the sequence of reactors should stop.

## 5.3. *The Optimal Choice of Temperature and Holding Time with a Single Reaction*

In considering the more general problem for a single reaction we will seek the minimum total holding time which will secure a given conversion. We have already seen in Section 5.1 that this is equivalent to seeking the maximum conversion for a given total holding time, so that both problems will be effectively solved together.

As before, let $f_R(c_{R+1})$ denote the minimum total holding time

$$\Theta_R = \sum_1^R \theta_r = \sum_1^R \frac{(c_r - c_{r+1})}{r(c_r, T_r)}$$

required to achieve an extent of reaction $c_1$ with feed state $c_{R+1}$. Then, as we have seen, the temperature policy is disjoint and the principle of optimality leads to the equation

$$f_R(c_{R+1}) = \text{Min} \left[ \frac{c_R - c_{R+1}}{R(c_R)} + f_{R-1}(c_R) \right] \tag{1}$$

where the minimization is to be attained by choice of $c_R$, $c_{R+1} \leq c_R \leq c_1$. Thus in a sequence of $R$ reactors there are $(R - 1)$ choices to be made, $c_R$, $c_{R-1}$, . . ., $c_2$. This corresponds to the fact that not all the $\theta_r$ can be arbitrarily chosen if the required extent $c_1$ is to be achieved. The sequence of equations (1) starts with a definite expression for $\theta_1$, no choice being possible when $R = 1$, namely,

$$f_1(c_2) = \frac{c_1 - c_2}{R(c_1)}. \tag{2}$$

Little more could be said of this problem, for such an iterated algorithm is simplicity itself to a digital computer, were it not that

71

the graphical presentation of the results is interesting. This depends on the fact that each term in $\Theta_R$, $(c_r - c_{r+1})/R(c_r)$, is the area of a rectangle of base $(c_{r+1},c_r)$ and height equal to the ordinate of the curve $1/R(c)$ at the upper end. This is shown in Fig. 5.4 where it is

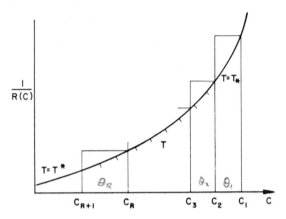

FIG. 5.4. Construction for the holding times of a sequence of reactors.

evident that given $c_{R+1}$ and $c_1$ the problem is to choose the intermediate extents $c_R, \ldots, c_2$ to minimize the area of the rectangles. In its alternative form the problem could lead to a question of maximizing the area of such a set of rectangles, and this is essentially the way Denbigh has presented it (1960). Furthermore, we notice that since the optimal temperature is a function only of $c$, the curve of $1/R(c)$ can be graduated in $T_m(c)$. This allows the corresponding optimal temperature to be read off when any choice of $c_r$ is made. We shall see in Chapter 7 that the area under the curve itself represents the minimum holding time for a tubular reactor, and it is already quite evident that this is approached as the number of stages, $R$, is increased indefinitely. For this reason we can quite logically denote the curve $1/R(c)$ by $\Gamma_\infty$, as is done in Fig. 5.5.

It is useful to follow the construction of the optimal policy in Fig. 5.5. In the case of one reactor Eq. (2) shows that no choice is needed; $\theta_1$ must be the area of the rectangle of base $(c_2,c_1)$ and height $1/R(c_1)$. Another way of saying this is that the vertex $[c_2,1/R(c_1)]$ must lie on the horizontal straight line $\Gamma_1$ through $[c_1,1/R(c_1)]$. Now suppose that $c_3$ is given and that by some means or other, to be discussed later, the optimal choice of $c_2$ has been made; then this

72

can be recorded by drawing the locus $\Gamma_2$ of the vertex $[c_3, 1/R(c_2)]$ as found for various $c_3$. When the curve $\Gamma_2$ is drawn (and it can be drawn smoothly through comparatively few points) $f_2(c_3)$ can be calculated quickly for any $c_3$ in $(0,c_1)$. It is simply a matter of drawing the

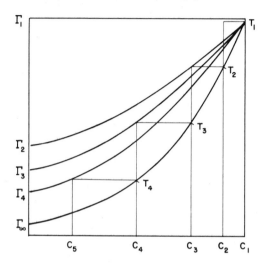

FIG. 5.5. Construction for the optimal holding times of a sequence of reactors.

ordinate through $(c_3,0)$ to the curve $\Gamma_2$, proceeding horizontally to $\Gamma_\infty$ and vertically to $\Gamma_1$; then $f_2$ is the sum of the areas of the two rectangles, and $T_2$ can be read off from the graduations on $\Gamma_\infty$. The measurement of the area of the rectangles can be avoided, for $\Gamma_2$ can be graduated in $f_2(c_3)$ and thus the value of $f_2$ can be read off at the vertex lying on $\Gamma_2$. $\Gamma_1$ can of course be graduated likewise. We may proceed in this way by solving Eq. (1) for $R = 3,4, \ldots$ to build up a set of curves $\Gamma_3, \Gamma_4, \ldots$ on which the upper left-hand vertex of the rectangle for stages $3,4, \ldots$ must lie. $\Gamma_r$ is the locus of $[c_{r+1}, 1/R(c_r)]$ where $c_r$ is chosen to satisfy Eq. (1). $\Gamma_r$ may be graduated in $f_r(c_{r+1})$.

The construction for the optimal policy is now very easily made, as the example for $R = 4$ in Fig. 5.5 shows. From the point $(c_5,0)$ we proceed vertically to $\Gamma_4$, horizontally to $\Gamma_\infty$, vertically to $\Gamma_3$, and so on to $\Gamma_1$. $f_4$ is read off from $\Gamma_4$ and the holding time of individual stages from the differences $\theta_r = f_r - f_{r-1}$. The corresponding temperature policy is found from the graduation of $\Gamma_\infty$.

Nothing has been said of the method of finding the $c_R$ that minimizes the right-hand side of Eq. (1). This may be done by trial and error or by a straightforward numerical search. The difficulty with these methods is that the minimum is rather shallow and it is difficult to pin down the optimum precisely. We do better to make use of the admirable differentiability of all our functions and the fact that the optimal $c_R$ must lie strictly in the open interval $(c_{R+1}, c_1)$; for $c_R = c_{R+1}$ means that there are only $(R - 1)$ reactors and $c_R = c_1$ that there is only one. In approaching the problem from this angle we shall also do away with another difficulty, namely, that the curves $\Gamma_r$ are attached rather strongly to the value of $c_1$ and would have to be recalculated if this value were changed.

We first observe that the optimal choice of $c_r$ is such that

$$\frac{\partial}{\partial c_r}\left(\sum_{s=1}^{k}\theta_s\right) = 0 \qquad \text{for} \quad 2 \le r \le k \tag{3}$$

and that this is true for all $k \le R$. Consequently,

$$\frac{df_R}{dc_{R+1}} = \frac{\partial}{\partial c_{R+1}}\left(\sum_{s=1}^{R}\theta_s\right) + \sum_{r=2}^{R}\frac{\partial}{\partial c_r}\left(\sum_{s=1}^{R}\theta_s\right)\frac{dc_r}{dc_{R+1}}$$

$$= \frac{\partial}{\partial c_{R+1}}\left(\sum_{s=1}^{R}\theta_s\right),$$

since the second term vanishes by (3), and therefore

$$\frac{df_R}{dc_{R+1}} = -\frac{1}{R(c_R)}. \tag{4}$$

Thus, for the minimum of the right-hand side of (1)

$$\frac{d}{dc_R}\left[\frac{c_R - c_{R+1}}{R(c_R)} + f_{R-1}(c_R)\right]$$

$$= \frac{1}{R(c_R)}\left[1 - c_R\frac{R'(c_R)}{R(c_R)}\right] + c_{R+1}\frac{R'(c_R)}{R^2(c_R)} - \frac{1}{R(c_{R-1})} = 0. \tag{5}$$

Consider the family of curves

$$h(c;c') = \frac{1}{R(c)}\left[1 - c\frac{R'(c)}{R(c)}\right] + c'\frac{R'(c)}{R^2(c)}. \tag{6}$$

Then the condition (5) for a minimum is

$$h(c_R;c_{R+1}) = \frac{1}{R(c_{R-1})}. \tag{7}$$

But the point $[c_R, 1/R(c_{R-1})]$ lies on the curve $\Gamma_{R-1}$; hence, for a

74

given $c_{R+1}$ the optimal $c_R$ is given by the intersection of $\Gamma_{R-1}$ and the member of the family $h$ for the given $c_{R+1}$. Figure 5.6 shows four members of the family corresponding to $c' = 0$, $c_1/4$, $c_1/2$, $3c_1/4$. Now $\Gamma_1$ can be drawn immediately, being a horizontal straight line. It intersects $h(c;c')$ at the value of $c_2$ which is optimal for $c_3 = c'$. Since $\Gamma_2$ is the curve $[c_3, 1/R(c_2)]$ we have only to drop from the inter-

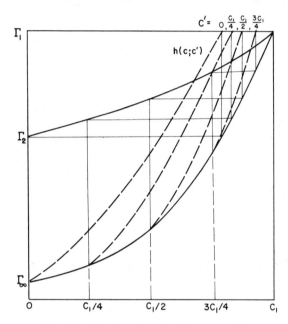

FIG. 5.6. Construction for the curves $\Gamma_r$.

section of $\Gamma_1$ and $h(c;c')$ to the curve $\Gamma_\infty$ and go horizontally to the ordinate through $c = c'$ to find a point on the curve $\Gamma_2$. From $\Gamma_2$ we obtain $\Gamma_3$ and so on. Moreover, the curves of the family $h$ can be drawn without reference to $c_1$ and so the construction can be done equally easily for any value of $c_1$.

It may be worth remarking in passing that Eq. (5.2.5) shows that a falling temperature sequence is always required with an exothermic reaction, for on differentiating this equation we have

$$\frac{dT_m}{dc} = -\frac{RT_m^2}{(-\Delta H)} \sum_{i=1}^{n} \frac{\alpha_i^2}{c_{i0} + \alpha_i c}$$

showing that $T_m$ decreases with increasing $c$.

## 5.4. Parametric Studies

In studying a given reaction it is often of great interest to vary some of the parameters. Such variations can arise naturally, as for example with varying grades of catalyst, and it is important to see how sensitive the optimal policy is. In the case of the simpler kinetic expressions it is possible to do a complete parametric study. With more complex systems a great deal of qualitative information may be given even though detailed calculation is out of the question; an excellent example of this is Horn's study of Denbigh's system (Horn, 1960). We shall content ourselves here with determining the least number of dimensionless parameters and providing the materials for a complete study to be made of any first-order reversible reaction.

Let $c_0 = \sum_1^n c_{i0}$ be the total concentration of all species and $\mu_i = c_{i0}/c_0$ the concentration fraction of $A_i$ in the reference composition. Then the extent of reaction, $c$, may be made dimensionless by dividing by $c_0$,

$$x = c/c_0. \tag{1}$$

Then Eq. (5.2.7) can be written

$$R(c) = c_0 A \prod_1^n (\mu_i + \alpha_i x)^{-\delta_i} = c_0 A P(x) \tag{2}$$

where

$$\delta_i = p\alpha_i - \beta_i = (E_1 \gamma_i - E_2 \beta_i)/(E_2 - E_1) \tag{3}$$

and

$$A = \frac{p^p}{(p+1)^{p+1}} \frac{k_1^{*p+1}}{k_2^{*p}} c_0^{(p+1)\beta - p\gamma - 1}, \tag{4}$$

$$\alpha = \sum_1^n \alpha_i, \quad \beta = \sum_1^n \beta_i, \quad \gamma = \sum_1^n \gamma_i. \tag{5}$$

$A$ has the dimensions of $(\text{time})^{-1}$ so that $P(x)$ is the dimensionless rate of reaction. The holding time can be made dimensionless by setting

$$\zeta = A\theta. \tag{6}$$

The temperature may be made dimensionless by dividing by $-\Delta H/R$, since only exothermic reactions are of interest. Then

$$\tau = \frac{RT}{-\Delta H} = \left[ \ln \kappa \prod_1^n (\mu_i + \alpha_i x)^{\alpha_i} \right]^{-1}, \tag{7}$$

where

$$\kappa = \frac{p+1}{p} \frac{k_2^*}{k_1^*} c_0^\alpha. \tag{8}$$

There are thus in general $(2n + 3)$ parameters, which fall into groups as follows: $p$, an exponent related only to the activation energy; $\kappa$ related to the kinetic constants and $c_0$; $\mu_i$ related to the initial or reference composition; $\beta_i$ related to the order of the reaction; and $\tau_*, \tau^*$ related to the bounds on the temperature. The equations governing the system when $\tau_* \leq \tau \leq \tau^*$ are

$$\zeta_r = (x_r - x_{r+1})/P(x_r) \tag{9}$$

$$\phi_R(x_{R+1}) = \operatorname{Min} \sum_1^R \zeta_r = \operatorname{Min} \left\{ \frac{x_R - x_{R+1}}{P(x_R)} + \phi_{R-1}(x_R) \right\} \tag{10}$$

and

$$\phi_1(x_2) = (x_1 - x_2)/P(x_1). \tag{11}$$

From the solution of these equations we can recover the optimal policy for $\theta$ and $T$ by setting

$$\theta_r = \zeta_r/A, \qquad T_r = \tau_r(-\Delta H)/R. \tag{12}$$

Applying this to the first-order reversible reaction $A_1 - A_2 = 0$, we have $c_0 = c_{10} + c_{20} = c_1 + c_2$ for the whole course of reaction. Thus $c_1/c_0 = x_1$, $c_2/c_0 = x_2$ and we can write for simplicity $x_1 = y$, $x_2 = 1 - y$. Then

$$P(y) = y^{-p}(1 - y)^{p+1} \tag{13}$$

is the dimensionless maximum reaction rate in which only one parameter, $p$, is involved. Figure 5.7 shows values of $1/P(y)$ for several values of $p$, since this is needed for constructing the optimal policy. The other set of functions needed for the construction is the family $h$, which in dimensionless form can be written

$$h(y;\eta) = h_1(y) + \eta h_2(y) = \frac{1}{P(y)} \left\{ 1 - y \frac{P'(y)}{P(y)} \right\} + \eta \frac{P'(y)}{P^2(y)}. \tag{14}$$

These functions can be obtained from Figs. 5.8 and 5.9 where they are shown for the same values of $p$. The optimal temperature is given by

$$\tau = [\ln \kappa y/(1 - y)]^{-1} \tag{15}$$

which is given for several values of $\kappa$ in Fig. 7.2. We thus have all the data required for a full study of the first-order reversible reaction.

77

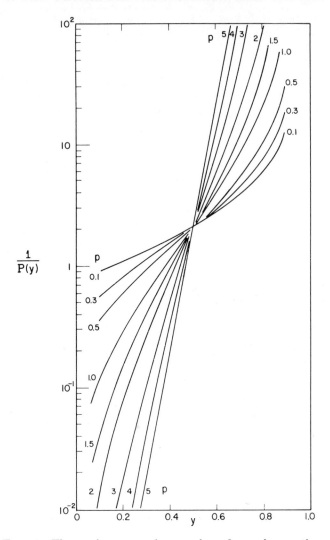

FIG. 5.7. The maximum reaction rate for a first-order reaction.

It is also evident that it is available also for reactions of any order between two chemical species.

## 5.5. *Two Consecutive Reactions*

We will continue the study of optimal problems with a stoichiometric objective function, for some of the tricks of the trade can be

78

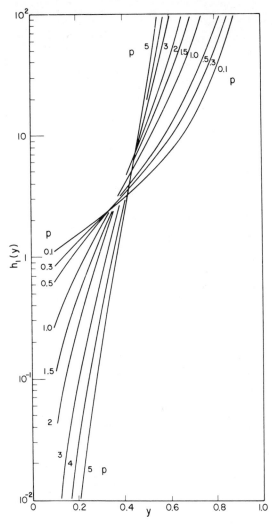

FIG. 5.8. The function $h_1(y)$.

demonstrated most easily in this context. It has been emphasized that dynamic programming is not a rote to be thoughtlessly applied to every problem, but that one of its best features is the play it allows the ingenuity in simplifying the complexities of the situation. The system of first-order consecutive reactions $A \rightarrow B \rightarrow C$, which has been studied by Amundson and Bilous (1956), is very suitable for the next step. The temperature policy is no longer disjoint and

79

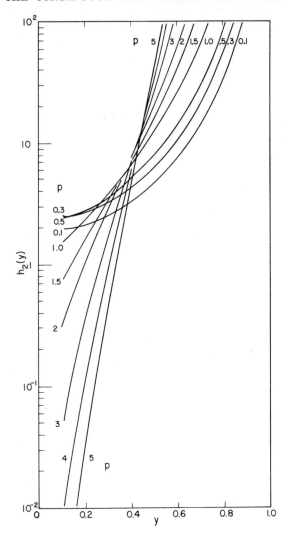

FIG. 5.9. The function $h_2(y)$.

two equations have to be considered in place of one, but the assumption of first-order reaction allows a valuable simplification.

As variables we will take the concentrations of A and B, denoting them by $x$ and $y$ respectively. Then if the reaction $A \rightarrow B$ proceeds at a rate $k_1 x$ and $B \rightarrow C$ at a rate $k_2 y$, we have

$$x_{r+1} = \{1 + \theta_r k_1(T_r)\} x_r, \tag{1}$$

$$y_{r+1} = -\theta_r k_1(T_r) x_r + y_r \{1 + \theta_r k_2(T_r)\}, \tag{2}$$

$$k_i(T) = k_i^* \exp\{-E_i/RT\}. \tag{3}$$

For brevity let

$$a_r = \theta_r k_1(T_r) \tag{4}$$

then

$$b_r = \theta_r k_2(T_r) = \rho_r a_r^{1/p} \tag{5}$$

where

$$p = E_1/E_2, \quad \rho_r = \theta_r^{(p-1)/p} k_1^{*-1/p} k_2^*. \tag{6}$$

(In Chapter 7 where the same system of reactions is discussed the symbol $r$ is used in place of $p$. With the suffix $r$ for the reactor it will be less confusing here to use $p$.) Except in the case $p = 1$, which is very special, it is convenient to use $a$ and $\rho$ as the variables in place of $\theta$ and $T$. This is possible since the Jacobian $\partial(a,\rho)/\partial(\theta,T)$ does not vanish.

We now observe that Eqs. (1) and (2) are homogeneous in $x$ and $y$, so that dividing one by the other

$$z_{r+1} = z_r \frac{1 + b_r}{1 + a_r} - \frac{a_r}{1 + a_r} \tag{7}$$

where

$$z_r = y_r/x_r. \tag{8}$$

Thus

$$z_r = \{(1 + a_r)z_{r+1} + a_r\}/(1 + b_r) \tag{9}$$

gives a relation for determining the output ratio $z_r$ at any stage in terms of the feed ratio $z_{r+1}$. The actual formation of B in reactor $r$ is given by

$$\frac{y_r - y_{r+1}}{x_{r+1}} = \frac{a_r}{1 + a_r} - \frac{b_r}{1 + a_r} z_r$$

$$= \frac{a_r}{(1 + a_r)(1 + b_r)} - \frac{b_r}{1 + b_r} z_{r+1}. \tag{10}$$

We seek the optimal conditions for the formation of B and so take as objective function

$$y_1 - y_{R+1} = \sum_1^R (y_r - y_{r+1}).$$

Let the maximum of this be

$$f_R(x_{R+1}, y_{R+1}) = \text{Max} \sum_1^R (y_r - y_{r+1}), \tag{11}$$

then because of the homogeneity of the equations this must be proportional to $x_{R+1}$ but otherwise only depend on the ratio $y_{R+1}/x_{R+1} = z_{R+1}$. We therefore let

$$f_R(x_{R+1}, y_{R+1}) = x_{R+1} g_R(z_{R+1}). \tag{12}$$

Now applying the principle of optimality to the function $f_R$ we obviously have

$$f_R(x_{R+1}, y_{R+1}) = \text{Max} \{(y_R - y_{R+1}) + f_{R-1}(x_R, y_R)\} \tag{13}$$

where the maximization is to be achieved by correct choice of $\theta_R$ and $T_R$, i.e., $a_R$ and $\rho_R$ or $a_R$ and $b_R$. If we now substitute (12) in (13), divide throughout by $x_{R+1}$, and make use of (10), we have

$$g_R(z_{R+1})$$
$$= \text{Max} \left\{ \frac{a_R}{(1 + a_R)(1 + b_R)} - \frac{b_R}{(1 + b_R)} z_{R+1} + \frac{1}{(1 + a_R)} g_{R-1}(z_R) \right\}. \tag{14}$$

In this equation all reference to $x$ and $y$ individually has disappeared and we have an equation in $z$ only, to be solved recursively in conjunction with (9).

For definiteness we will consider only the case of constant holding time $\theta_r$, for which $\rho$ is also a constant independent of $r$. Consider first the single reactor:

$$g_1(z_2) = \text{Max} \left\{ \frac{a_1}{(1 + a_1)(1 + \rho a_1^{1/p})} - \frac{\rho a^{1/p}}{1 + \rho a^{1/p}} z_2 \right\}. \tag{15}$$

If it is within the permissible range of temperature, which for the moment we will take to be very great, the expression on the right-hand side has an extremum when

$$z_2 = \frac{p + (p - 1)\rho a_1^{1/p} - \rho a_1^{(p+1)/p}}{\rho a_1^{(1-p)/p}(1 + a_1)^2}. \tag{16}$$

In case $0 < p < 1$ this is a maximum and has the value

$$g_1(z_2) = a_1(1 - p + a_1)/(1 + a_1)^2 \tag{17}$$

where of course $a$ is determined as a function of $z_2$ by (16). This is shown in Fig. 5.10 for $p = 0.5$; the curve rising from left to right is $g_2$ given by (17), while those descending from left to right are several members of the family (16). For any $z_2$, whose scale is on the left, $a_1$ can be determined by the appropriate curve $\rho$, as can $g_1$ by ascending to the other curve.

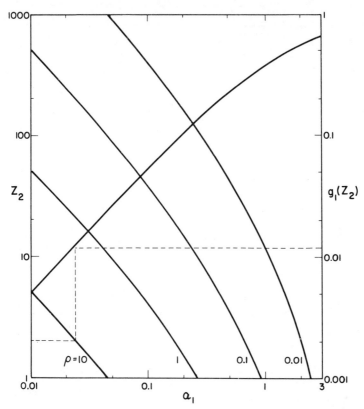

FIG. 5.10. Single-stage optimal conditions for two consecutive reactions.

Figure 5.11 illustrates a graphical approach to the solution of (14). It can claim no great accuracy but may be useful in determining just where the regions of interest lie. The positive horizontal and negative vertical scales are of $z$, and the other two are of $g$. In the first quadrant the curves $g_1(z_2)$, $g_2(z_3)$, . . . will be successively constructed. Let us start with $g_1(z_2)$ already known and construct the quantity to be maximized in the right-hand side of (14) for $z_3 = 2$ and $a = 1$. The point A has ordinate $z = 2$, and in the third quadrant is drawn the line $a = 1$ of the family (10)

$$\frac{a}{(1 + a)(1 + b)} - \frac{b}{(1 + b)} z.$$

It is inconvenient to draw the whole family of such lines, so an arbitrary tie line is drawn in this case with coordinates where the

83

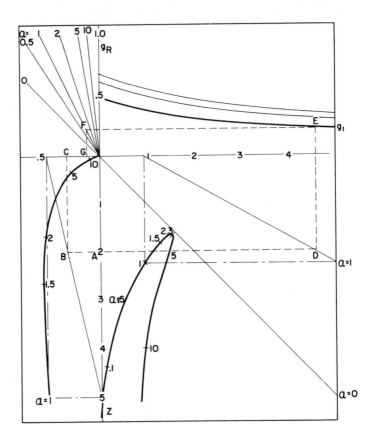

FIG. 5.11. Graphical construction for the functional equation (5.5.14).

line of the family intersects the axes. This tie line is graduated in $a$, and by dropping perpendiculars onto the two axes the line of the family with corresponding $a$ can immediately be drawn. The abscissa of B is thus the first term on the right side of (14). The construction of $z_2$ from $z_3$ is done in the fourth quadrant by the line of the family (9)

$$\frac{1+a}{1+b} z + \frac{a}{1+b}.$$

Here the tie line is constructed from the abscissa of the intersection of the line with the horizontal axis of $z$ and the ordinate of its intersection with the vertical $z = 5$. If it were desirable such tie lines

84

could be drawn for various values of $\rho$; those here correspond to $\rho = 0.1$. If the temperature is restricted to within the bounds $T_*, T^*$, then only the part of the tie line between $a_* = a(T_*)$ and $a^* = a(T^*)$ need appear. The point D then has the abscissa $z_2$ and so the ordinate of E is $g_1(z_2)$. In the second quadrant the family of lines of slope $-(1 + a)^{-1}$ are used to construct the second term in (14), namely $g_1(z_2)/(1 + a_1)$, whose value is then the abscissa of the point G. By this means we can estimate the two terms of (14) and hence their sum for any chosen $a$. A small amount of trial and error will rapidly locate the maximizing value.

When $p > 1$ the right-hand side of (14) begins by decreasing from zero, and since for large $a$ its value approaches $-z_{R+1}$ it may never be positive. In case of a single reactor the extrema will still be given by Eq. (16) but we now see that the right-hand side of this equation has a maximum. This maximum is

$$z_c = \frac{(p - 1)^2}{4\rho} \left\{ 1 + \frac{1}{\rho} \left( \frac{p - 1}{p + 1} \right)^{-(p+1)/p} \right\} \tag{18}$$

and occurs when $a = (p - 1)/(p + 1)$. Thus if $z_2 > z_c$ it is unprofitable to react, for this will always lead to a net loss of B. If $z_2 < z_c$ there will be two values of $a$ satisfying Eq. (16) of which the larger gives the maximum. But this maximum will give a positive value of $g_1$ [Eq. (17)] only if $a_1 > (p - 1)$, and for this

$$z_2 < \rho^{-1} p^{-1} (p - 1)^{(p-1)/p}.$$

The calculation proceeds as in the case $p > 1$ but it is clear that there will be a more severe restriction on $z$.

## 5.6. Denbigh's System of Reactions

In his contribution to the First European Symposium on Chemical Reaction Engineering, Denbigh (1958) propounded a most elegant system of reactions which demonstrated the great improvement that can result from optimal policies. He regards A as a valuable raw material in the production of Y by the reaction scheme:

A + B —(1)→ X —(3)→ Y  
   |          |  
  (2)     (4)  
   ↓         ↓  
   P        Q

85

X is an intermediate and P and Q waste products whose formation it is important to minimize. The reactions are taken to be first order with respect to the concentrations of A and X, so that we have here a system which is kinetically simpler than its stoichiometry would lead one to suppose. The reaction rate constants of the four reactions are of the usual form,

$$k_i = k_1^* \exp \{ -E_i/RT \} \qquad i = 1,2,3,4,$$

and it is on the relative values of the four activation energies that the optimal policy depends.

All rate constants $k_i$ increase with increasing temperature, but $k_i$ will increase more rapidly than $k_j$ if and only if $E_i > E_j$. With this in mind we may distinguish the following cases:

I. $E_1 > E_2, E_3 > E_4$: Here increasing temperature will promote reactions 1 and 3 by comparison with the side reactions 2 and 4. We may therefore expect a conversion of nearly all A to Y, with a sufficiently high operating temperature.

II. $E_1 < E_2, E_3 < E_4$: Here the lowest possible temperature will give the best yield.

III. $E_1 > E_2, E_3 < E_4$: In the early stages of the reaction before much X has been formed it is important to make reaction (1) dominate reaction (2), so that a high temperature is called for. Later on in the course of the reaction it is reaction (3) which is to be emphasized at the expense of (4), and this requires a lower temperature. Hence a decreasing sequence of temperatures is desirable.

IV. $E_1 < E_2, E_3 > E_4$: In this case the same argument calls for an increasing temperature sequence.

The first two of these cases are not very interesting; it is the second pair that arouses our curiosity. Following Denbigh we shall consider case (IV) and use his relations $E_2 = E_1 + 6000$, $E_3 = E_1$, $E_4 = E_1 - 6000$. [Horn (1960) has made a full study of this case for the tubular reactor and has given a general discussion of the variation of optimal policy with the parameters.] Denbigh demonstrated that for a single reactor the greatest yield of Y was 25 per cent of the feed A, obtained at a temperature of 326 °K. With two reactors, the first at 280 °K and the second at the highest possible temperature, the yield was just over 57 per cent. We shall recover Denbigh's results by dynamic programming and go on to the case

## 5.6. DENBIGH'S SYSTEM OF REACTIONS

of three reactors, and then consider the effect of restrictions on the temperature and holding time.

We will again work in concentration, rather than extent, variables and denote by $a, x, y$ the concentrations of A, X, and Y respectively. A suffix $r$ applies to values in reactor $r$, of which the holding time is $\theta_r$ and the temperature $T_r$. Then a mass balance of A, X, and Y gives the equations

$$a_{r+1} = a_r\{1 + \theta_r(k_{1r} + k_{2r})\} \tag{1}$$

$$x_{r+1} = -a_r\theta_r k_{1r} + x_r\{1 + \theta_r(k_{1r} + k_{2r})\} \tag{2}$$

$$y_{r+1} = \quad\quad - x_r\theta_r k_{3r} + y_r. \tag{3}$$

The equations are simplified if we take the variables

$$\rho = k_2/k_1, \qquad \sigma = \theta k_1. \tag{4}$$

The other rate constants can always be expressed in the form $p\rho^q$ but we will take Denbigh's values

$$k_3/k_1 = 10^{-2} \qquad k_4/k_3 = \rho^{-1}. \tag{5}$$

The temperature and holding time can always be recovered from $\rho$ and $\sigma$ for

$$T = (E_2 - E_1)/R \ln (k_2^*/\rho k_1^*) \tag{6}$$

$$\theta = \sigma\{\rho^{-E_1}k_1^{*-E_2}k_2^{*E_1}\}^{1/(E_2-E_1)}. \tag{7}$$

Then Eqs. (1)–(3) become

$$a_{r+1} = \{1 + \sigma_r(1 + \rho_r)\}a_r \tag{8}$$

$$x_{r+1} = -\sigma_r a_r + \{1 + 10^{-2}\sigma_r\rho_r^{-1}(1 + \rho_r)\}x_r \tag{9}$$

$$y_{r+1} = \quad\quad - 10^{-2}\sigma_r x_r + y_r. \tag{10}$$

Again we notice that these equations are homogeneous in the concentrations, so that we can deal in their ratios. Let

$$a_r/a_{r+1} = 1/(1 + \alpha_r) \tag{11}$$

$$x_r/a_r = \xi_r = \zeta_r^{-1} \tag{12}$$

$$(y_r - y_{r+1})/a_{r+1} = \eta_r. \tag{13}$$

Then the basic equations can be written

$$\alpha_r = \sigma_r(1 + \rho_r) \tag{14}$$

$$\xi_r = L_r + \xi_{r+1}M_r \tag{15}$$

$$\eta_r = Y_r + \xi_{r+1}Z_r \tag{16}$$

87

where

$$L_r = 100Z_r = \frac{\alpha_r}{1 + \rho_r} \{1 + (\alpha_r/100\rho_r)\}^{-1} \tag{17}$$

$$M_r = (1 + \alpha_r) \{1 + (\alpha_r/100\rho_r)\}^{-1} \tag{18}$$

$$Y_r = 10^{-2} \frac{\alpha_r^2}{(1 + \alpha_r)(1 + \rho_r)^2} \{1 + (\alpha_r/100\rho_r)\}^{-1}. \tag{19}$$

Before formulating the dynamic program we will consider a single stage and see how to maximize $\eta_1$, the yield of Y. In the first place $\eta_1$ is a monotonic increasing function of $\alpha_1$ so that $\alpha_1$ should be made as large as possible. This means that $a_1$ should be as small as possible or that the reaction should go to completion. In common with Denbigh and Horn we will assume that this can be achieved. For any given $\alpha_1$, $\eta_1$ will be maximum when $\rho_1$ is so chosen that

$$\xi_2 = \frac{\alpha_1}{1 + \alpha_1} \frac{200\rho_1^2 - \alpha_1(1 - \rho_1)}{(\alpha_1 - 100\rho_1^2)(1 + \rho_1)}. \tag{20}$$

For constant $\xi_2$ the solution curves of this relation lie in a very narrow band of the $\alpha,\rho$ plane, namely, between the curves $\alpha = 200\rho^2/(1 - \rho)$ $(\xi = 0)$ and $\alpha = 100\rho^2(\xi = \infty)$. The behavior of the optimal temperature may be rather more accurately portrayed if we plot $\alpha/100\rho^2$ against $\rho$ for constant $\xi$. This is shown in Fig. 5.12,

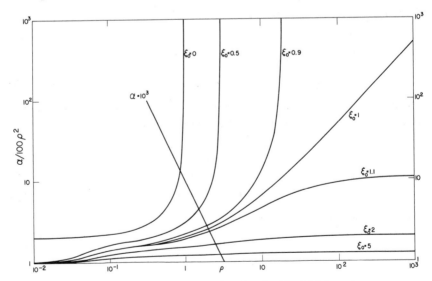

FIG. 5.12. Single-stage optimal policy for Denbigh's system.

and for any $\alpha$ the corresponding optimal temperature is given by the intersection of the appropriate curve for constant $\xi$ and the straight line of $\alpha/100\rho^2$, of which one is shown. As $\alpha \to \infty$ this line moves to distant parts of the plane and so intersects the curves of constant $\xi$ on their asymptotes. Thus in this case we have

$$\xi_2 \leq 1, \qquad \rho_1 = \left(\frac{1 + \xi_2}{1 - \xi_2}\right), \qquad \eta_1 = \tfrac{1}{4}(1 + \xi_2)^2,$$

$$\xi_2 > 1, \qquad \rho_1 = \infty, \qquad \eta_1 = \xi_2. \tag{21}$$

In fact $\rho_1$ can never become infinite, but if its limiting value $k_2^*/k_1^*$ is very large these simple formulas will be approximately true: this we shall assume.

We are seeking the greatest yield of Y and so take as an objective function $y_1 - y_{R+1} = \sum_1^R (y_r - y_{r+1})$. Let

$$f_R(a_{R+1}, x_{R+1}) = \text{Max} \sum_1^R (y_r - y_{r+1}) \tag{22}$$

then by the principle of optimality

$$f_R(a_{R+1}, x_{R+1}) = \text{Max} \{y_R - y_{R+1} + f_{R-1}(a_R, x_R)\} \tag{23}$$

where an optimal choice of only $\alpha_R$ (or $\sigma_R$) and $\rho_R$ has to be made. If we make use of the homogeneity of the situation we can write, as in the previous section,

$$f_R(a_{R+1}, x_{R+1}) = a_{R+1} g_R(\xi_{R+1}) \tag{24}$$

so that the equation to be solved for $g_R$ becomes

$$g_R(\xi_{R+1}) = \text{Max} \left\{\frac{y_R - y_{R+1}}{a_{R+1}} + \frac{a_R}{a_{R+1}} g_{R-1}(\xi_R)\right\}$$

$$= \text{Max} \{\eta_R + g_{R-1}(\xi_R)/(1 + \alpha_R)\}. \tag{25}$$

In the solution of this equation, however, there lies a considerable practical difficulty. The quantity $\xi_R$ is liable to take on very high values if in the first stage X is formed from A with little waste. This means that in calculating $g_R$ for a given $\xi_{R+1}$ we need values of $\xi_R$ which are far greater than the given $\xi_{R+1}$—a situation that makes for difficulty of interpolation and consequent inaccuracy, but which can be overcome by a device of Bellman's. We introduce also the variable $\zeta = \xi^{-1}$ [see Eq. (12)] and agree to use the one which lies between 0 and 1, so that in the bad situation where we want large values of $\xi$ we are saved by working with small values of $\zeta$.

Along with $\zeta$ we introduce another homogeneous form of the objective function and write

$$f_R(a_{R+1}, x_{R+1}) = a_{R+1} g_R(\xi_{R+1}) = x_{R+1} h_R(\zeta_{R+1}). \tag{26}$$

Then in place of Eq. (23) we have four equations to be used according as $\xi_{R+1}$ and $\xi_R$ are greater or less than one. They are:

$$\xi_{R+1} \leq 1, \quad \xi_R \leq 1: \qquad g_R(\xi_{R+1}) = \text{Max}\left\{\eta_R + \frac{1}{1 + \alpha_R} g_{R-1}(\xi_R)\right\}$$

$$\xi_{R+1} \leq 1, \quad \xi_R \geq 1: \qquad g_R(\xi_{R+1}) = \text{Max}\left\{\eta_R + \frac{\xi_R}{1 + \alpha_R} h_{R-1}(\zeta_R)\right\}$$

$$\tag{27}$$

$$\xi_{R+1} \geq 1, \quad \xi_R \leq 1: \qquad h_R(\zeta_{R+1}) = \text{Max}\left\{\eta_R \zeta_{R+1} + \frac{\zeta_{R+1}}{1 + \alpha_R} g_{R-1}(\xi_R)\right\}$$

$$\xi_{R+1} \geq 1, \quad \xi_R \geq 1: \qquad h_R(\zeta_{R+1}) = \text{Max}\left\{\eta_R \zeta_{R+1} + \frac{\xi_R \zeta_{R+1}}{1 + \alpha_R} h_{R-1}(\zeta_R)\right\}.$$

In all these $\eta_R$, $\xi_R$ are calculated by Eqs. (15) and (16) and the maximization is by variation of $\alpha_R$ and $\rho_R$, from which $T_R$ and $\theta_R$ can be calculated. For a single reactor with complete reaction, $\alpha_1 \to \infty$ and Eq. (21) may be written

$$g_1(\xi_2) = \tfrac{1}{4}(1 + \xi_2)^2, \qquad h_1(\zeta_2) = 1. \tag{28}$$

This is shown in Fig. 5.13.

TABLE 5.1

Optimal Policies for Denbigh's Reactions

| Number of reactors | Temperatures | | | "Holding times" | | | Yield |
|---|---|---|---|---|---|---|---|
| (R) | $T_3$ | $T_2$ | $T_1$ | $\sigma_3$ | $\sigma_2$ | $\sigma_1$ | (%) |
| With no restrictions | | | | | | | |
| 1 | — | — | 326 | — | — | $\infty$ | 25 |
| 2 | — | 280 | $\infty$ | — | 4.0 | $\infty$ | 57.4 |
| 3 | 270 | 320 | $\infty$ | 1.6 | 0.8 | $\infty$ | 66.3 |
| With restrictions on temperature and holding time | | | | | | | |
| 1 | — | — | 318 | — | — | 340 | 22.1 |
| 2 | — | 276 | 394 | — | 2.82 | 2100 | 45.1 |
| 3 | 260 | 288 | 394 | 1.4 | 1.3 | 2100 | 49.5 |

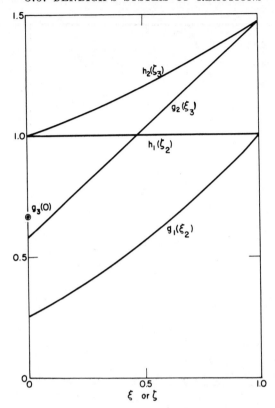

FIG. 5.13. Optimal yield without restraint.

The solution of Eqs. (27) has been carried as far as three stages with a feed of pure A + B ($\xi_4 = 0$), and is summarized in Table 5.1 and Figs. 5.13 and 14. The first two lines of Table 5.1 agree with Denbigh's result that the maximum yield from one reactor of 25 per cent is increased to 57 per cent in two if the first is at 280 °K and the second at a much higher temperature. The third line shows that three stages yield 66 per cent with a properly increasing sequence of temperatures. The holding times are given as values of $\sigma$ and cannot be translated into the actual holding time without assuming values for $k_1^*$ and $E_1$. Table 5.1 gives values for $\xi_{R+1} = 0$ only, but Fig. 5.13 shows the optimal yield for all $\xi$ for one and two reactors. In Fig. 5.14 the optimal policy is given and is extracted as follows. In solving Eqs. (27) say for $\xi_4 = 0$, $R = 3$ the optimal values of $\alpha_3$ and $\rho_3$ will have been obtained and consequently the value of $\xi_3$ or $\zeta_3$. These are

91

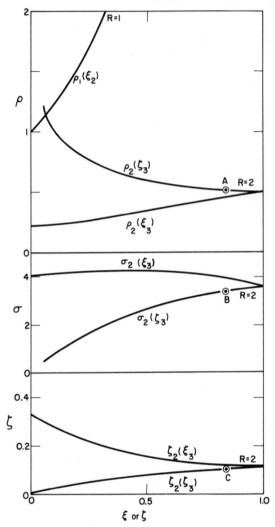

FIG. 5.14. Optimal policy without restraint.

not shown in the figure but it is found that $\zeta_3 = 0.84$ and so we can find the remaining conditions from Fig. 5.14. $\rho_2 = 0.51$ is given by the point A with abscissa $\zeta = 0.84$ and $\sigma_2 = 3.4$ by the point B. The point C shows that $\zeta_2 = 0.1$ so that for the last stage the optimal conditions are to have a vessel as large as possible ($\alpha_1$ large) and a temperature as high as possible ($\rho_1$ large).

The assumptions that the last reactor can be made infinitely large and operated at an infinite temperature is of course unrealistic and it is interesting to see what effect some natural restrictions would have on the optimal policy and yield. We will assume that the temperature must lie between two limits $T_*$ and $T^*$ and that the holding time is not greater than $\theta^*$. In this case $\rho$ must lie between its values calculated for the two temperatures and $\sigma$ must not exceed a value depending on $\rho$, given by Eq. (4):

$$\rho_* \leq \rho \leq \rho^* \tag{29}$$

$$\sigma \leq \theta^* k_1 = \sigma^* \rho^q \tag{30}$$

where $q = E_1/(E_2 - E_1)$ and

$$\sigma^* = \theta^* \{k_1^{*E_2} k_2^{*-E_1}\}^{1/(E_2 - E_1)}.$$

Equations (29) and (30) together imply that

$$\alpha \leq \sigma^* \rho^q (1 + \rho). \tag{31}$$

These restrictions limit the permissible values of $\alpha$ and $\rho$ to the region of the $\alpha,\rho$ plane shown in Fig. 5.15. In this region the bounding curves $\xi_2 = 0$ and $\xi_2 = \infty$ of Eq. (20) are shown. Since we know that for a single reactor $\alpha_1$ should be made as large as possible, the

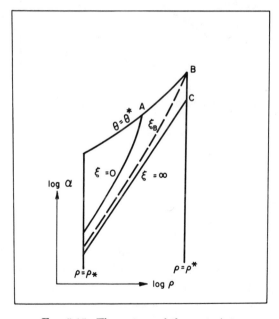

FIG. 5.15. The nature of the restraints.

optimal conditions for a single stage must lie on the part ABC of the boundary of this region. On the part AB the restriction on the holding time is the limiting one, whereas on the part BC it is the temperature which is at its upper bound. The dividing line for Denbigh's constants, $q = 1$, $\rho_* = 0$, $\rho^* = 5$, $\sigma^* = 420$ comes for $\xi = 0.914$. $g_1$ and $h_1$ can be calculated by working back from any point of the arc ABC using Eqs. (16) and (20); they are shown in Fig. 5.16.

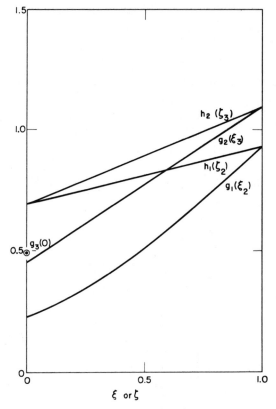

FIG. 5.16. Optimal yield with restraint.

Comparing Fig. 5.16 with Fig. 5.13 we see that the restraint has quite an appreciable effect on the optimal yield. Figure 5.17 shows the optimal policy under restraint and may be compared with Fig. 5.14. In the lower section of Table 5.1 the details of the optimal

94

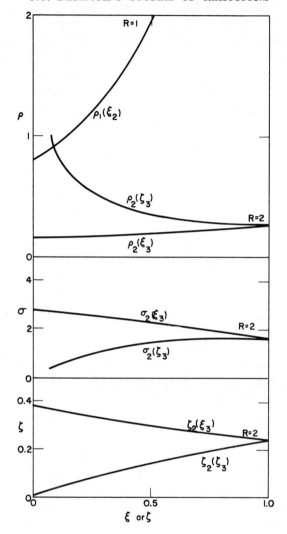

FIG. 5.17. Optimal policy with restraint.

policy for the restricted case are given. It is evident that the restriction does have a significant effect on both the yield and the policy, but the general character of the improvement of yield by the use of several stages is maintained.

## 5.7. *General Problems with Sequences of Stirred Tanks*

With these particular examples before us we are in a position to give a general algorithm for optimal design in sequences of stirred tanks. The basic equations have been given in Section 3.2 and need not be derived again. They are:

$$c_{r+1}^j - c_r^j + \theta_r r^j(c_r^k, T_r) = 0$$

$$j = 1, \ldots m \qquad (1)$$

$$T_{r+1} - T_r + \theta_r \sum_{j=1}^m H^j r^j(c_r^k, T_r) - Q_r' = 0 \qquad (2)$$

where the $c_r^j$ are the extents of the $m$ reactions in reactor $r$, $H^j$ is proportional to the heat of the $j$th reaction and $Q_r'$ to the rate of heat removal from reactor $r$. An alternative set of equations (3.2.11 and 3.2.12) can be written down in terms of the concentrations of $m$ of the species. This set of $(m + 1)$ equations can be regarded in two ways. If $\theta_r$ and $T_r$ are specified, the $m$ Eqs. (1) can be solved to give $c_r^j$ in terms of $c_{r+1}^j$ and then Eq. (2) can be solved for the rate of heat removal required to maintain this temperature. A more direct view of these equations takes account of the fact that in practice it is the holding time $\theta_r$ and rate of heat removal $Q_r'$ that are fixed by the design. Thus we can also regard Eqs. (1) and (2) as a set of $(m + 1)$ simultaneous equations which, given any $\theta_r$ and $Q_r'$, may be solved for $c_r^j, T_r$ in terms of $c_{r+1}^j, T_{r+1}$. This second form is the more difficult of the two, not merely on account of the fact that there are $(m + 1)$ instead of $m$ equations but because of the essentially nonlinear way in which $T$ enters the equations. Though they appear less direct, it is better on the whole to use the first approach and regard $\theta_r$ and $T_r$ as the design variables of each stage. If the value of $Q_r'$ that is called for is impossible this implies a restriction on $\theta_r$ and $T_r$.

Let $q$ be the flow rate of the reactants through the system and $v(c^1, \ldots c^m)$ their value per unit volume. Then

$$q\{v(c_1^1, \ldots c_1^m) - v(c_{R+1}^1, \ldots c_{R+1}^m)\}$$

is the increase in value of the process stream. The costs enumerated in Section 4.3 can be calculated for each reactor when any choice

96

of $\theta_r$ and $T_r$ has been made. Let us write the total cost of reactor as $C_r(q,\theta_r,T_r)$. Then the net profit of the whole operation is

$$P_R = \sum_1^R p_r = \sum_1^R [q\{v(c_r^1, \ldots c_r^m) - v(c_{r+1}^1, \ldots c_{r+1}^m)\} - C_r(q,\theta_r,T_r)].$$
(3)

$P_R$ is a function of (i) the feed state $c_{R+1}^1, \ldots c_{R+1}^m$, $T_{R+1}$, (ii) the flow rate $q$, (iii) the operating variables $\theta_1, \ldots \theta_R$, $T_1, \ldots T_R$, and our objective is to maximize it by suitable choice of the last two sets of variables. As has been pointed out before, the flow rate $q$ is on a different basis from the others as it does not vary from stage to stage, and also it may have to be fixed by other considerations. Let

$$f_R(c_{R+1}^k, T_{R+1};q) = \text{Max } P_R,$$
(4)

where the maximization is by choice of the $2R$ quantities $\theta_r$ and $T_r$. By the principle of optimality

$$f_R(c_{R+1}^k, T_{R+1};q) = \text{Max } \{p_R + f_{R-1}(c_R^k, T_R;q)\}.$$
(5)

In Eq. (5) only $\theta_R$ and $T_R$ (or $Q_R'$) have to be chosen and the sequence of equations is started by the obvious remark that with no reactors there is no profit, or

$$f_0(c_1^k, T_1;q) = 0.$$
(6)

When this function has been found it may be possible to choose $q$ to give the maximum

$$F_R(c_{R+1}^k, T_{R+1}) = \text{Max } f_R(c_{R+1}^k, T_{R+1};q).$$
(7)

In many cases it may be of great advantage to preheat the process stream before it enters the first reactor. If $T_0$ is the temperature of the feed stock, we may suppose that the cost of this will be a function of $q$ and $T_{R+1} - T_0$, say $H(T_{R+1} - T_0, q)$. We should now seek the maximum

$$G_R(c_{R+1}^k, T_0) = \underset{q}{\text{Max}} \underset{T_{R+1}}{\text{Max}} [f_R(c_{R+1}^k, T_{R+1};q) - H(T_{R+1} - T_0, q)]$$
(8)

by first choosing $T_{R+1}$ optimally and then $q$.

The individual steps and cost estimations may be somewhat lengthy, as indicated in Section 4.4, but are well within the power of a digital computer. The major difficulty in a problem of this kind is that a function of $(m + 1)$ variables has to be calculated, stored and interpolated. A device that is sometimes used to overcome this

97

difficulty is that of fitting a polynomial approximation to the function. This requires the storage of only a few coefficients. However, it is only safe to apply when a thorough understanding of the shape of the surface has been attained.

## 5.8. *Sequences of Stirred Tanks with Bypassing of the Feed Stream*

A modification of the stirred tank sequence deserving a little attention is that in which part of the process stream is diverted from the feed and passes to later stages before reacting. Clearly, the proportion of bypass must be rather nicely chosen if it is to be of any advantage at all. There are reasons however for supposing that something might be gained, at any rate in the case of a single exothermic reaction. We know that this requires a falling temperature gradient and it may be that a very economical way of attaining this is by simply bypassing cold feed.

The situation we have in mind is illustrated in Fig. 5.18. Of the

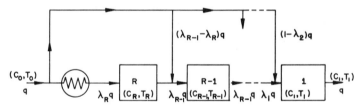

FIG. 5.18. The stirred tank sequence with bypassing.

feed flowing at rate $q$ and temperature $T_0$ only a fraction $\lambda_R q$ is passed to the first reactor and this is preheated to a temperature $T_{R+1}$ before entering it. The stream leaving reactor $R$ is mixed with a fraction $(\lambda_{R-1} - \lambda_R)q$ of the original feed before entering reactor $(R - 1)$, or, since these are stirred tanks, the stream of original feed may go straight to reactor $(R - 1)$. This mixing takes place between each stage, $\lambda_r q$ being the flow through reactor $r$; $\lambda_1 = 1$.

The necessary modifications to the steady-state equations have been given in Section 3.2. In terms of the extents of the $m$ reactions the equations are

$$\lambda_{r+1} c_{r+1}^j - \lambda_r c_r^j + (\lambda_r - \lambda_{r+1}) c_0^j + \theta_r r^j (c_r^k, T_r) = 0 \qquad (1)$$

98

and

$$\lambda_{r+1}T_{r+1} - \lambda_r T_r + (\lambda_r - \lambda_{r+1})T_0 + \theta_r \sum_1^m H^j r^j - Q'_r = 0 \qquad (2)$$

where

$$\theta_r = V_r/q. \qquad (3)$$

$\theta_r$ is the nominal holding time of reactor $r$; the actual mean residence time of the reactants in this reactor is $\theta_r/\lambda_r$.

In the general optimal problem we now have to choose $3R$ quantities: the volumes $V_R, \ldots V_1$, the temperatures $T_{R+1}, \ldots T_1$, and the bypass ratios $\lambda_R, \ldots \lambda_2$. If $v(c^1, \ldots c^m)$ is the value function, the net gain in value at stage $r$ is

$$q\{\lambda_r v(c_r^1, \ldots c_r^m) - \lambda_{r+1}v(c_{r+1}^1, \ldots c_{r+1}^m) - (\lambda_r - \lambda_{r+1})v(c_0^1, \ldots c_0^m)\}.$$

The cost of the reactor will be estimated as in the preceding section, $C_r(\theta_r, T_r, \lambda_r q)$, so that the net profit from reactor $r$ is

$$p_r = q\{\lambda_r \bar{v}(c_r^1, \ldots c_r^m) - \lambda_{r+1}\bar{v}(c_{r+1}^1, \ldots c_{r+1}^m)\} - C_r(\theta_r, T_r, \lambda_r q), \qquad (4)$$

where

$$\bar{v}(c^1, \ldots c^m) = v(c^1, \ldots c^m) - v(c_0^1, \ldots c_0^m). \qquad (5)$$

Again we may let

$$f_R(c_{R+1}^k, T_{R+1}, q) = \operatorname{Max} \sum_1^R p_r, \qquad (6)$$

the maximum profit sequence of reactors without the preheater. Applying the principle of optimality we have the equation

$$f_R(c_{R+1}^k, T_{R+1}, q) = \operatorname{Max} \{p_R + f_{R-1}(c_R^k, T_R, q)\}. \qquad (7)$$

This maximization is to be attained by correctly choosing $\theta_R, T_R$ (or $Q'_R$) and $\lambda_{R+1}$. The choice of $\lambda_{R+1}$ is of course restricted by $\lambda_{R+1} \le \lambda_R$ and $\lambda_1 = 1$. It is often convenient to work in the ratio $\mu_{R+1} = \lambda_{R+1}/\lambda_R$ when the restriction becomes $\mu_r \le 1, r = 2, \ldots R$. From any such choice, $c_R^k, Q'_R$ (or $T_R$) and so $p_R$ can be calculated. Only in the case where $c_{R+1}^k = c_0^k$ does the ratio $\lambda_{R+1}$ become meaningless; this corresponds to the fact that we would certainly not heat up part of the feed and promptly cool it again by mixing with cold feed.

Again, if $H(T_{R+1} - T_0, \lambda_R q)$ is the cost of preheating the feed, the final optimum is obtained as

$$G_R(c_0^k, T_0) = \operatorname*{Max}_q \operatorname*{Max}_{T_{R+1}} \{f_R(c_0^k, T_{R+1}, q) - H(T_{R+1} - T_0, \lambda_R q)\}. \qquad (8)$$

99

If $Q'_r = 0$, $r = 1, \ldots R$, so that no heat is added to or removed from the reactor $r$ by direct interchange, we may speak of the sequence of reactors as adiabatic. Then only $2R$ operating quantities can be chosen, $\theta_r$, $\lambda_r$ and $T_{R+1}$. This follows from the fact that with $Q'_r = 0$ Eqs. (1) and (2) can be solved for $c^k_r$ and $T_r$ in terms of $c^k_{r+1}, T_{r+1}$ when only $\lambda_{r+1}$ and $\theta_r$ are prescribed. The case of an adiabatic sequence with a single reaction admits of an elementary exposition, and this we will now give.

## 5.9. *The Adiabatic Sequence of Reactors with a Single Reaction*

We will consider the single exothermic reaction $\sum_1^n \alpha_i A_i = 0$ taking place in an adiabatic sequence of reactors of equal volume. Since such a reaction demands a decreasing temperature gradient there is good hope that bypassing cold feed will be a considerable help in improving the yield. In any event the system has the virtue of simplicity. Without loss of generality we can take the extent of reaction in the feed to be zero; $c_0 = 0$. Then Eqs. (5.8.1) and (5.8.2), with the assumption $\theta_r = \theta$, $r = 1, \ldots R$, become

$$\lambda_{r+1}c_{r+1} - \lambda_r c_r + \theta r(c_r, T_r) = 0 \tag{1}$$

and

$$\lambda_{r+1}T_{r+1} - \lambda_r T_r + (\lambda_r - \lambda_{r+1})T_0 + \theta H r(c_r, T_r) = 0. \tag{2}$$

It is convenient to take a new temperature variable of the same dimensions as $c$,

$$t = (T - T_0)/H. \tag{3}$$

With the variables $c$ and $t$ the two equations are

$$\lambda_r c_r - \lambda_{r+1}c_{r+1} = \lambda_r t_r - \lambda_{r+1}t_{r+1} = \theta r(c_r, t_r) \tag{4}$$

or

$$c_r - \mu_{r+1}c_{r+1} = t_r - \mu_{r+1}t_{r+1} = \theta r(c_r, t_r)/\lambda_r \tag{5}$$

where

$$\mu_{r+1} = \lambda_{r+1}/\lambda_r. \tag{6}$$

If we think of $t$ and $c$ as coordinates in a plane the state of the stream at any stage is represented by a point and the origin corresponds to the feed state $c = 0$, $T = T_0$. The point $(\mu t, \mu c)$ lies on the straight line through the origin and the point $(t,c)$, which we will call the ray through $(t,c)$. It represents the state of a mixture of two quantities of reactants of states $(t,c)$ and $(0,0)$ in proportions $\mu$ and $(1 - \mu)$ respectively. Let $\bar{c}_r = \mu_{r+1}c_{r+1}$ and $\bar{t}_r = \mu_{r+1}t_{r+1}$; then Eq. (5) reads

$$c_r - \bar{c}_r = t_r - \bar{t}_r = \theta r(c_r,t_r)/\lambda_r. \qquad (7)$$

It relates the product state $(t_r,c_r)$ to the feed state $(\bar{t}_r,\bar{c}_r)$ of reactor $r$, and shows that in the $t,c$ plane these two points lie on a line of unit slope of length proportional to $r$. This is illustrated in Fig. 5.19 for

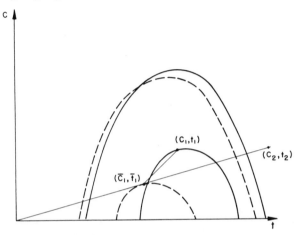

FIG. 5.19. The single-stage optimum.

a single reactor. $(t_2,c_2)$ is the state of the stream before mixture in a proportion $\mu_2:(1 - \mu_2)$ with feed. $\bar{c}_1 = \mu_2 c_2$, $\bar{t}_1 = \mu_2 t_2$ is the state of the feed to reactor 1 and $c_1,t_1$ the state of its product.

Let us set the problem of maximizing the extent of reaction, $c_1$, in the final product. We shall need to separate the adiabatic part of the sequence from the preheater and put

$$f_R(c_{R+1},t_{R+1}) = \text{Max } c_1. \qquad (8)$$

Since $\lambda_1 = 1$ and ultimately $c_{R+1}$ will be put equal to zero, we can write this as $\sum_1^R (\lambda_r c_r - \lambda_{r+1}c_{r+1})$, which by Eq. (4) is $\theta \sum_1^R r(c_r,t_r)$. Applying the principle of optimality we have

$$f_R(c_{R+1},t_{R+1}) = \text{Max } \{\lambda_R c_R - \lambda_{R+1}c_{R+1} + f_{R-1}(c_R,t_R)\}$$
$$= \text{Max } \{\theta r(c_R,t_R) + f_{R-1}(c_R,t_R)\}. \qquad (9)$$

Figure 5.19 shows the way immediately to $f_1(c_2,t_2)$. The full curves of that figure are loci of constant $r(c,t)$, the lower curve representing

101

a greater value of $r$ than the upper one. The broken curves are loci of inlet conditions $\bar{t}, \bar{c}$ that for a reactor holding time $\theta$ lead to a constant reaction rate. A point on the broken curve corresponding to the feed lies below and to the left of the point corresponding to the product by a distance $\theta r_1$. Now

$$f_1(c_2, t_2) = \text{Max } (\lambda_1 c_1 - \lambda_2 c_2) = \text{Max } \theta r(c_1, t_1) \tag{10}$$

and

$$c_1 - \mu_2 c_2 = t_1 - \mu_2 t_2 = \theta r(c_1, t_1)$$

since $\lambda_1 = 1$. Thus, given $(t_2, c_2)$ we want to find the point $(\bar{t}_1, \bar{c}_1)$ on the ray through it which maximizes $r(c_1, t_1)$. Since the lower curves are for higher reaction rates, the best point $(\bar{t}_1, \bar{c}_1)$ is clearly where the ray is tangent to one of the broken curves. This also shows that $f_1(c_2, t_2)$ is really a function only of the ratio $c_2/t_2$ and so is constant along a ray. By doing this for a number of rays we can plot the locus $\overline{\Gamma}_1$ of optimal inlet conditions and $\Gamma_1$ of corresponding product conditions. Then given any state $(t_2, c_2)$ we have only to join the point to the origin and find at the intersection of this ray with $\overline{\Gamma}_1$ the best inlet conditions. Drawing a line of unit slope from this point to the curve $\Gamma_1$ gives the product. The value of $\mu_2$ is given by the ratio of the distance along the ray to $\overline{\Gamma}_1$ to the distance to $(t_2, c_2)$. The curves $\Gamma_1$ and $\overline{\Gamma}_1$ are shown in Fig. 5.20. $f_1(c_2, t_2) \equiv 0$ for any point to the left of $\overline{\Gamma}_1$.

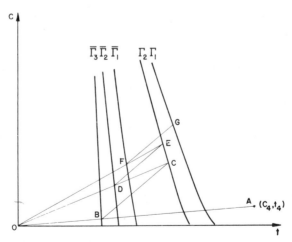

FIG. 5.20. The construction of the optimal policy.

For $f_2$ we have the equation

$$f_2(c_3, t_3) = \text{Max} \{ \theta r(c_2, t_2) + f_1(c_2, t_2) \} \tag{11}$$

where

$$c_2 - \mu_3 c_3 = t_2 - \mu_3 t_3 = \theta r(c_2, t_2)/\lambda_2. \tag{12}$$

In looking for this maximum we may as well look for it in the easiest possible way, namely, along a ray. Since $f_1$ is constant along a ray the maximum will be found at the point where the ray is tangent to a curve of constant reaction rate (full curve in Fig. 5.19). Thus $\Gamma_2$, the locus of conditions $t_2, c_2$, is the locus of tangent points of rays to the curves of constant $r$, and may be easily found. According to Eq. (12) the corresponding feed point $\bar{c}_2 = \mu_3 c_3$, $\bar{t}_2 = \mu_3 t_3$ lies below and to the right by a distance $r(c_2, t_2)/\lambda_2$. The value of $\lambda_2 = \mu_2$ is known from the one-stage policy and so the locus $\overline{\Gamma}_2$ of $(\bar{c}_2, \bar{t}_2)$ can be calculated. In this way a sequence of curves $\Gamma_r$ and $\overline{\Gamma}_r$ can be built up on which inlet and exit conditions for reactor $r$ must lie. We notice that by their construction $\Gamma_3$, $\Gamma_4$, etc., will all coincide with $\Gamma_2$.

The way in which such a diagram may be used is shown in Fig. 5.20 for three stages. The point A, $(t_4, c_4)$, represents the state of the partially reacted feed which is to be blended with cold unreacted feed. To find this blended feed we join A to the origin and take the intersection with $\overline{\Gamma}_3$, B; $\mu_4$ is the ratio OB/OA. To find the product $(t_3, c_3)$ we take a line of unit slope through B to $\Gamma_3 = \Gamma_2$, and the intersection C is the required point. Continuing in this way, D lies on OC and $\overline{\Gamma}_2$ and $\mu_3 = $ OD/OC; DE is of unit slope and E lies on $\Gamma_2$; F lies on OE and $\overline{\Gamma}_1$ and $\mu_2 = $ OF/OE; finally, the product state is G on $\Gamma_1$. From the values of $\mu$ the values of $\lambda$ may be calculated. $\lambda_1 = 1$, $\lambda_2 = \mu_2$, $\lambda_3 = \mu_3 \mu_2$, $\lambda_4 = \mu_4 \mu_3 \mu_2$.

Such a diagram is useful up to the penultimate reactor $(R - 1)$; for the last stage we have to consider the cost of preheater. For the reactor $R$ it is a matter of choosing the temperature $t_{R+1}$ which is most economical. Since $c_{R+1} = 0$ we have

$$c_R = t_R - t_{R+1} = \theta r(c_R, t_R)/\lambda_R, \tag{13}$$

that is, the point $(t_R, c_R)$ lies above and to the right of $(t_{R+1}, 0)$ by a distance $\theta r_R/\lambda_R$. To find the point $(t_R, c_R)$ we start from any point on the $t$ axis (see Fig. 5.21, point M) and draw a line of unit slope. $(t_R, c_R)$ is the point N which satisfies Eq. (13) with the value of $\lambda_R$

appropriate to the optimal $(R-1)$-stage policy. Thus a locus of N can be drawn corresponding to values of $t_{R+1}$ in the interval KL. L is the point of intersection of $\overline{\Gamma}_{R-1}$ with the $t$ axis and it is evident that it is not worth proceeding beyond this point. K is the point

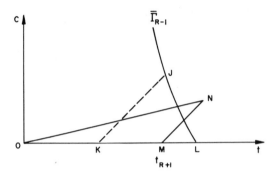

FIG. 5.21. The optimal preheat temperature.

$(t_{R+1},0)$ corresponding to J, $(t_R,c_R)$, for which $\lambda_R = 1$. If $h(t_{R+1})$ is the cost of preheating to the temperature $t_{R+1}$ as a fraction of the value of the product of unit extent, the final optimal policy is obtained by finding the $t_{R+1}$ for which $f_{R-1}(c_R,t_R) - h(t_{R+1})$ is maximum, and $c_R,t_R$ is related to $t_{R+1}$ by (13). If $h(t_{R+1})$ is proportional to $t_{R+1}$, the interval KL could be graduated in the constant of proportionality.

Such a construction as this is only useful in the case of stoichiometric objective functions, but it does give a simple presentation of the complete optimal policy. We shall find this presentation useful in the next chapter.

# The Multibed
# Adiabatic Reactor

---

*"There is Thingumbob shouting!" the Bellman said.*
*"He is shouting like mad, only hark!*
*He is waving his hands, he is wagging his head,*
*He has certainly found a Snark!"*

---

IN THIS CHAPTER we shall consider several design problems for converters consisting of adiabatic beds with cooling between stages. This cooling will be either by interchanger or by mixing with a bypass of cold unreacted feed. The first case allows analytical relationships to be taken rather farther than we might expect, but the second depends upon numerical evaluation from an early stage. If there is only one reaction taking place the design lends itself to the kind of graphical presentation we have noticed in Sections 3.3 and 5.9. Later in the chapter we shall consider simultaneous reactions and cold-shot cooling by a reaction mixture different from the feed.

In any event the design of an $R$-bed reactor requires the choice of $2R$ variables. In the case of interchanger cooling these may be taken to be the $R$ bed sizes and $R$ inlet temperatures. With the first bed this may involve heating of the cold feed with appropriate cost, whereas between succeeding beds the interchanger cost will depend on the amount of heat to be removed. In the case of the cold shot reactor the $R$ bed sizes, the $(R - 1)$ bypass rates, and the inlet temperature to the first bed must be chosen. With several beds and realistic estimates of cost this would present a formidable problem to any method other than dynamic programming. With the simple estimates of cost that we shall use to begin with, an immediate insight into the structure of the optimal design can be gained. Simple though these cost estimates are they can be reinterpreted as Lagrange multipliers to solve a number of other problems. The decision of just how many beds should be used in a reactor may also be made optimally on the basis of this study.

This chapter has been worded from the point of view of an exothermic reaction for which cooling between stages is needed. If the reaction were endothermic, heating between stages would be required and the same design analysis would go through. However, it is doubtful if an adiabatic converter is really the best type to use in this case, for the greatest possible temperature is required and the heat would be better used in maintaining this throughout the course of reaction.

## 6.1. Interchanger Cooling with a Single Reaction

For a single reaction with the simplifying assumption of a mean specific heat, the equations of Section 3.3 give

$$dc/dt = r(c,T) \tag{1}$$

$$T = T_i + H(c - c_i). \tag{2}$$

Here $c$ is the extent of reaction, $T$ the temperature and $t$ the holding time from the inlet of the bed, $H = (-\Delta H)/C_p$ and the suffix $i$ denotes inlet values. As mentioned in Chapter 3 the situation can be illustrated in the $c,T$ plane, and Fig. 6.1 does so for a simple first-order reaction

$$r = k_1 - (k_1 + k_2)c$$

with

$$k_1 = \exp\left\{19 - \frac{12{,}000}{T}\right\}, \qquad k_2 = \exp\left\{41 - \frac{25{,}000}{T}\right\} \tag{3}$$

and

$$H = 10^3.$$

The broken lines are adiabatic paths given by Eq. (2). The equilibrium line $\Gamma_e$, on which $r = 0$, is shown and also the locus $\Gamma_m$, of maximum reaction rate within an adiabatic bed. If $c_m,T_m$ is a point on this curve, it provides a natural origin on the adiabatic path through it. This path can then be graduated in the holding time

$$\theta = \int_{c_m}^{c} \frac{dc}{r[c,T_m + H(c - c_m)]} \tag{4}$$

106

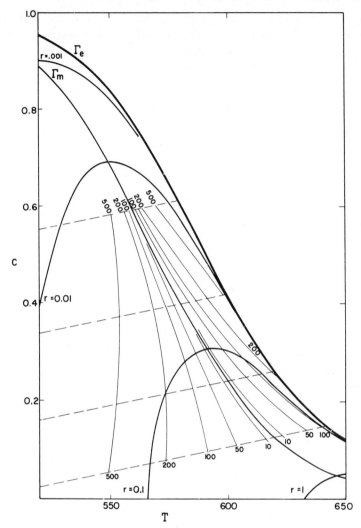

FIG. 6.1. The $c,T$ plane for a reversible first order reaction.

required to take the extent of reaction from $c_m$ to $c$. The figure shows the curves of constant $\theta$ for $\pm\theta = 10, 50, 100, 200, 500$. Loci of constant reaction rate ($r = 1, 10^{-1}, 10^{-2}, 10^{-3}$) are also shown. Such a diagram could be used for a rapid trial-and-error search for an optimal design, for it is intuitively evident that the adiabatic paths should lie across the line $\Gamma_m$. However, we shall show that such trial and error is unnecessary.

107

## 6. THE MULTIBED ADIABATIC REACTOR

The $R$ beds of the reactor will be numbered from the last to the first, and a prime used to denote the exit conditions. Thus $c_r, T_r$ is the state of the feed to bed $r$ and $c'_r, T'_r$ the exit state. The holding time $\theta_r$ of this bed will be given by

$$\theta_r = \int_{c_r}^{c'_r} \frac{dc}{r(c, T_r + H(c - c_r))} = \int_{c_r}^{c'_r} \frac{dc}{r_r(c)}. \tag{5}$$

Since there is no reaction in the interchanger,

$$c_r = c'_{r+1}. \tag{6}$$

It is consistent with this notation to denote the feed state by $c'_{R+1}, T'_{R+1}$ so that the total increase in the extent of reaction will be $c'_1 - c'_{R+1}$. If we use a material objective function and associate with each chemical species $A_i$ a value $v_i$, the increase in value is given by $v(c'_1 - c'_{R+1})$, where $v = \sum_{i=1}^{n} v_i \alpha_i$ and the $\alpha_i$ are the stoichiometric coefficients. If $q$ is the flow rate through the reactor, $qv(c'_1 - c'_{R+1})$ is the rate at which the value of the process stream is increasing. We will assume that the cost of a bed is proportional to its volume $q\theta_r$ and write the unit cost as $\lambda v$. Likewise for the interchanger the cost is to be proportional to the amount of heat removed or added, namely $qC_p|T'_{r+1} - T_r|$, and the unit cost will be $\mu v/C_p$. Thus the objective function of total gain minus total cost is

$$P_R = qv(c'_1 - c'_{R+1}) - \lambda qv \sum_1^R \theta_r - \mu qv \sum_1^R |T'_{r+1} - T_r| = qv \sum_1^R p_r \tag{7}$$

where

$$p_r = c'_r - c_r - \lambda \theta_r - \mu |T'_{r+1} - T_r|. \tag{8}$$

In writing this last expression for the profit from each stage we have made use of (6). It will become clear that we can use a different cost for heating than for cooling if this is desirable.

The problem may thus be stated as follows: Given $c'_{R+1}, T'_{R+1}$ we wish to maximize $\sum_1^R p_r$ by correct choice of $\theta_1, \ldots \theta_R$ and $T_1, \ldots T_R$. Since $\theta_R$ is expressed rather more directly in terms of $c'_r$ than vice versa an equivalent and slightly simpler formulation is to choose $c'_1, \ldots c'_R$ and $T_1, \ldots T_R$. Let

$$f_R(c'_{R+1}, T'_{R+1}) = \text{Max} \sum_1^R p_r$$

$$= \text{Max} \sum_1^R \left[ \int_{c_r}^{c'_r} \left\{ 1 - \frac{\lambda}{r_r(c)} \right\} dc - \mu |T'_{r+1} - T_r| \right]. \tag{9}$$

108

Then applying the principle of optimality we have immediately

$$f_R(c'_{R+1}, T'_{R+1})$$

$$= \text{Max} \left[ \int_{c_R}^{c'_R} \left\{ 1 - \frac{\lambda}{r_R(c)} \right\} dc - \mu |T'_{R+1} - T_R| + f_{R-1}(c'_R, T'_R) \right]. \quad (10)$$

In this equation the maximization is by correct choice of $c'_R$ and $T_R$ and we shall show that even these two choices can be made successively rather than simultaneously.

We begin with one bed, for which

$$f_1(c'_2, T'_2) = \text{Max} \left[ \int_{c_1}^{c'_1} \left\{ 1 - \frac{\lambda}{r_1(c)} \right\} dc - \mu |T'_2 - T_1| \right]. \quad (11)$$

Suppose that $T_1$ has been chosen so that, since $c_1 = c'_2$, $r_1(c) = r(c, T_1 + H(c - c_1))$ is a known function. The choice of $c'_1$ is then clear, for

$$\frac{\partial p_1}{\partial c'_1} = 1 - \frac{\lambda}{r_1(c'_1)} = 0$$

requires the exit condition $c'_1, T'_1$ to lie on the locus $(c, rT) = \lambda$. This is the curve ABC shown in the upper part of Fig. 6.2. The part BC of this curve is obviously undesirable for the end point of the bed for it means that the whole reaction has taken place in a region where the rate of reaction is less than $\lambda$ and so has been entirely unprofitable. The part AB of this curve is denoted by $\Gamma'_1$.

Consider the integral

$$I(c_1, T_1) = \int_{c_1}^{c'_1} \left\{ 1 - \frac{\lambda}{r_1(c)} \right\} dc \quad (12)$$

where $c'_1$ is always chosen to lie on $\Gamma'_1$. $c_1 = c'_2$ is fixed and we want to study the variation of $I$ with $T_1$. This is shown in Fig. 6.2. If we take $T_1$ to be the point A, the intersection of $c = c_1$ and $\Gamma'_1$, then the integral vanishes. If we take $T_1$ at K such that the adiabatic path goes through B, the intersection of $\Gamma_m$ and $\Gamma'_1$, then $I$ will be negative. Certainly there are paths, such as EF, MN or CD, for which $I$ is positive and since it is continuous there must be some path GH for which $I = 0$. Thus the form of $I$ as a function of $T_1$ is as shown in the lowest section of the figure, a hump lying between the values of $T_1$ corresponding to A and G. On this section of the figure is also drawn the function $\mu |T_1 - T'_2|$ which is a wedge with vertex at $T_1 = T'_2$.

Now

$$p_1 = I(c_1, T_1) - \mu |T_1 - T'_2|$$

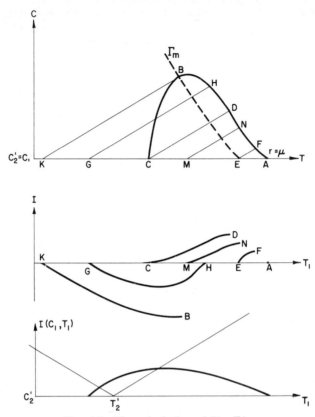

FIG. 6.2. The calculation of $I(c_1, T_1)$.

and $T_1$ has to be chosen to maximize this, which is a matter of elementary geometry. According to Fig. 6.3 we can distinguish seven values of $T_1$ that have particular interest. They are:

$T_1^*$, where the tangent at $T_3^*$ meets the axis,
$T_2^*$, where $I = 0$ for the first time,
$T_3^*$, where the tangent to the curve has slope $\mu$,
$T_4^*$, the position of the maximum of $I$,
$T_5^*$, where the tangent to the curve has slope $-\mu$,
$T_6^*$, where $I = 0$ the second time,
$T_7^*$, where the tangent at $T_5^*$ meets the axis.

If $T_2'$ is outside the interval $(T_1^*, T_7^*)$ then the curve of $I$ lies wholly beneath the wedge and so $p_1$ is negative whatever choice of $T_1$ is made. Physically this means that the initial state is so hot or so cold

110

that at the "cost" of cooling or heating, $\mu$, it is not worthwhile to react. If $T_2'$ lies within the interval $(T_1^*, T_3^*)$ then $T_1$ should be chosen equal to $T_3^*$. If $T_3^* \leq T_2' \leq T_5^*$ then the greatest value of $p_1$ lies immediately above the vertex of the wedge and $T_1 = T_2'$: no heating or cooling

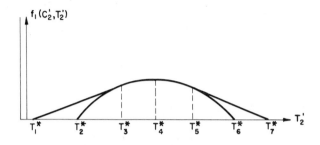

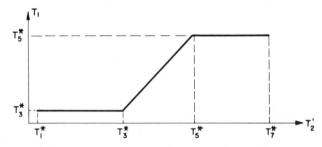

FIG. 6.3. The optimal yield and inlet temperature policy for fixed $c_2'$.

is needed. If $T_2'$ lies within the interval $(T_5^*, T_7^*)$ then cooling is needed and $T_1$ should be chosen equal to $T_5^*$. $T_4^*$ is the point to which both $T_3^*$ and $T_5^*$ tend as $\mu \to 0$. It is the optimal choice of inlet temperature when heating or cooling does not cost anything. $T_2^*$ and $T_6^*$ are of interest in the sense that if $\mu$ exceeds the slopes of the tangents at these points, it is never of profit to heat or cool.

This optimal policy for the choice of $T_1$ is shown in the lower part of Fig. 6.3. It follows that

$$
f_1(c_2', T_2') = \begin{cases} I(c_2', T_3^*) - \mu(T_3^* - T_2'), & T_1^* \leq T_2' \leq T_3^*, \\ I(c_2', T_2'), & T_3^* \leq T_2' \leq T_5^*, \\ I(c_2', T_5^*) - \mu(T_2' - T_5^*), & T_5^* \leq T_2' \leq T_7^*, \end{cases} \quad (13)
$$

and that it is zero outside $(T_1^*, T_7^*)$. But this simply means that $f_1$ is the curve $I$ beveled off with its two tangents of slopes $\pm\mu$. This

111

# 6. THE MULTIBED ADIABATIC REACTOR

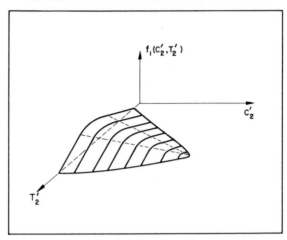

FIG. 6.4. The optimal yield surface.

construction has been done for fixed $c_1 = c_2'$, but clearly it can be repeated for any $c_2'$ and will generate such a surface as is shown in Fig. 6.4. In the same way the loci of $T_3^*$ and $T_5^*$ as $c_2'$ varies will be found and may be plotted as curves $\Gamma_{1*}$ and $\Gamma_1^*$ as in Fig. 6.5. This allows the complete optimal policy to be constructed very quickly. If the state $(c_2', T_2')$ is at such a point as A to the left of the curve $\Gamma_{1*}$, it is necessary to heat first to B and then to react to C. If the initial state lies, as D does, between the two branches of $\Gamma_1$ no heating or cooling is needed, one simply reacts to E. If the state is repre-

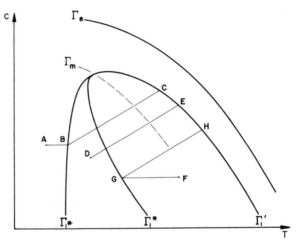

FIG. 6.5. The optimal policy for a single bed.

sented by F, cooling is needed to G and reaction to H. The curve $\Gamma_1'$ could be graduated in the value of $I$ for the path between $\Gamma_1^*$ or $\Gamma_{1*}$ and $\Gamma_1'$. Since $|T_2' - T_1|$ is the length of the line AB or FG it will then be easily possible to compute $f_1$ from Eq. (13).

This construction has been performed *in extenso* as it shows the structure of the optimal policy very clearly. For practical computation however one would work backwards from $\Gamma_1'$. If we differentiate $p_1$ with respect to $T_1$ and keep $(c_1', T_1')$ always on $\Gamma_1'$ we have

$$\frac{\partial p_1}{\partial T_1} = \lambda \int_{c_1}^{c_1'} \left( \frac{1}{r^2} \frac{\partial r}{\partial T} \right) dc \pm \mu.$$

Thus this is zero when

$$J(c_1, T_1) = \int_{c_1}^{c_1'} \left( \frac{1}{r^2} \frac{\partial r}{\partial T} \right) dc = \mp \frac{\mu}{\lambda} \tag{14}$$

and the integral can be calculated by integrating back from the intersection of the adiabatic with $\Gamma_1'$. Horn has given this relation in the case $\mu = 0$ (Horn and Küchler, 1959).

In preparation for the next stage we note that the derivatives of $f_1$ can be easily calculated. Suppose that $(c_2', T_2')$ lies between the two branches of the curve $\Gamma_1$ so that

$$f_1(c_2', T_2') = I_1(c_2', T_2') = \int_{c_1}^{c_1'} \left\{ 1 - \frac{\lambda}{r(c, T_2' + H(c - c_2'))} \right\} dc. \tag{15}$$

Thus

$$\frac{\partial f_1}{\partial T_2'} = \lambda J(c_2', T_2') \tag{16}$$

and

$$\frac{\partial f_1}{\partial c_2'} = -H\lambda J(c_2', T_2') - \left\{ 1 - \frac{\lambda}{r(c_2', T_2')} \right\}. \tag{17}$$

If $(c_2', T_2')$ lies to the left of $\Gamma_{1*}$ then by Eq. (13)

$$f_1(c_2', T_2') = \int_{c_1}^{c_1'} \left\{ 1 - \frac{\lambda}{r(c, T_1 + H(c - c_1))} \right\} dc - \mu(T_1 - T_2')$$

where $c_1 = c_2'$ and $T_1 = T_3^*(c_1)$ is a function of $c_2'$ only. In this case

$$\partial f_1 / \partial T_2' = \mu \tag{18}$$

$$\frac{\partial f_1}{\partial c_2'} = \{ \lambda J(c_1, T_1) - \mu \} \frac{dT_1}{dc_2'} - H\lambda J(c_1, T_1) - \left\{ 1 - \frac{\lambda}{r(c_1, T_1)} \right\}$$

$$= -H\mu - \left\{ 1 - \frac{\lambda}{r(c_1, T_1)} \right\} \tag{19}$$

since $J(c_1, T_1) = \mu/\lambda$. A similar result, but with $-\mu$ in place of $\mu$, is obtained in the case where $c_2', T_2'$ lies to the right of $\Gamma_1^*$. All these formulas, (16)–(19), can be reduced to two, namely:

$$\frac{\partial f_1}{\partial T_2'} = \lambda J(c_1, T_1) \tag{20}$$

and

$$\frac{\partial f_1}{\partial c_2'} = -H\lambda J(c_1, T_1) - \left\{1 - \frac{\lambda}{r(c_1, T_1)}\right\}, \tag{21}$$

for in the case of (16) and (17) $c_1 = c_2'$, $T_1 = T_2'$ while in the other cases $\lambda J$ is $\mu$ or $-\mu$. In all cases

$$\frac{\partial f_1}{\partial c_2'} + H \frac{\partial f_1}{\partial T_2'} = -\left\{1 - \frac{\lambda}{r(c_1, T_1)}\right\}, \tag{22}$$

and this is the derivative with respect to $c_2'$ along an adiabatic path.

Proceeding now to consider two adiabatic beds we have to solve the equation

$$f_2(c_3', T_3') = \text{Max} \left[ \int_{c_2}^{c'_2} \left\{1 - \frac{\lambda}{r_2(c)}\right\} dc - \mu |T_2 - T_3'| + f_1(c_2', T_2') \right]. \tag{23}$$

Again we suppose that $T_2$ has been chosen so that the adiabatic path is fixed. Then differentiating with respect to $c_2'$ along the adiabatic we have

$$\frac{\partial}{\partial c_2'} [p_2 + f_1(c_2', T_2')] = \left\{1 - \frac{\lambda}{r(c_2', T_2')}\right\} - \left\{1 - \frac{\lambda}{r(c_1, T_1)}\right\}. \tag{24}$$

This is zero when

$$r(c_2', T_2') = r(c_1, T_1), \tag{25}$$

so that the rate of reaction at the exit of the first bed should be the same as that at the inlet to the next, a fact that was first brought to light by Horn and Küchler (1959). Naturally, the point $(c_2', T_2')$ is not to be identical with $c_1, T_1$ for this would imply that the two beds were one, but we can see from the nature of the curves of constant $r(c, T)$ how the exit condition may be found. We take any point on $\Gamma_1^*$ (see Fig. 6.6) and continue the curve $r(c, T) = r(c_1, T_1) = r_1$ until $c = c_1$ again. This gives a point $(c_2', T_2')$ on the curve $\Gamma_2'$, the locus of the optimal exit conditions from bed 2.

We might now proceed to calculate $I(c_2, T_2)$ for various $T_2$ and $c_2 = c_3'$. As before, it will evidently be a humped curve like the lower part of Fig. 6.2. It follows that $I_2(c_2, T_2) + f_1(c_2', T_2')$ would be a dis-

114

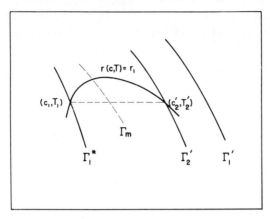

FIG. 6.6. The calculation of the inlet conditions to a second bed.

tortion of $f_1$ as if it had grown a fresh hump. Consequently $f_2$, as given by (23), is a beveled-off hump just like $f_1$ but lying above it. The points where the tangent in the $T$ direction have slopes $\pm\mu$ have the same interpretation: their loci form the branches, $\Gamma_2^*$ and $\Gamma_{2*}$, of the curve on which the inlet conditions of the first bed should lie. The graphical construction for the optimal policy is shown in Fig. 6.7, where the points A and L represent initial states that

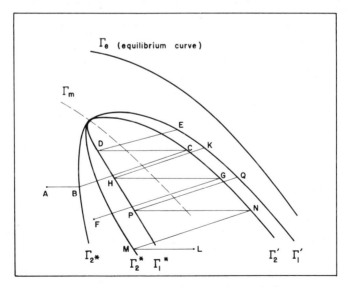

FIG. 6.7. The optimal policy with two beds.

115

require heating and cooling respectively before reaction, and F is a condition where it is most profitable to react immediately.

We may calculate the position of the branches of the curve $\Gamma_2$ analytically as follows:

$$\frac{\partial}{\partial T_2}\{I(c_2,T_2) + f_1(c_2',T_2')\}$$

$$= \lambda J(c_2,T_2) + \left\{1 - \frac{\lambda}{r(c_2',T_2')}\right\}\frac{\partial c_2'}{\partial T_2} + \frac{\partial f_1}{\partial c_2'}\frac{\partial c_2'}{\partial T_2} + \frac{\partial f_1}{\partial T_2'}\frac{\partial T_2'}{\partial T_2}$$

$$= \lambda J(c_2,T_2) + \left[\left\{1 - \frac{\lambda}{r(c_2',T_2')}\right\} - \left\{1 - \frac{\lambda}{r(c_1,T_1)}\right\}\right]\frac{\partial c_2'}{\partial T_2}$$

$$+ \lambda J(c_1,T_1)\left\{\frac{\partial T_2'}{\partial T_2} - H\frac{\partial c_2'}{\partial T_2}\right\}$$

$$= \lambda J(c_2,T_2) + \lambda J(c_1,T_1) = \lambda J(c_2,T_2) - \mu \qquad (26)$$

since (24) holds, $T_2' - Hc_2' = T_2 - Hc_2$ and for cooling between stages $\lambda J(c_1,T_1) = -\mu$. Thus differentiating the quantity to be maximized in (23) and setting the derivative equal to zero we find that $\Gamma_2^*$ is the locus $J(c_2,T_2) = 0$ and $\Gamma_{2*}$ that of $J(c_2,T_2) = 2\mu/\lambda$, with $(c_2',T_2')$ lying always on $\Gamma_2'$.

It is a remarkable fact that the derivatives of $f_2$ can also be worked out analytically. After some careful manipulation we have

$$\frac{\partial f_2}{\partial c_3'} = -\left\{1 - \frac{\lambda}{r(c_2,T_2)}\right\} - H[\lambda J(c_2,T_2) - \mu] \qquad (27)$$

$$\frac{\partial f_2}{\partial T_3'} = \lambda J(c_2,T_2) - \mu \qquad (28)$$

and hence in an adiabatic direction

$$\frac{\partial f_2}{\partial c_3'} + H\frac{\partial f_2}{\partial T_3'} = -\left\{1 - \frac{\lambda}{r(c_2,T_2)}\right\}. \qquad (29)$$

It follows that a curve $\Gamma_3'$ on which the exit conditions from the first of three beds should lie can be constructed from $\Gamma_2^*$ just as $\Gamma_2'$ was constructed from $\Gamma_1^*$. From $\Gamma_3'$ two branches of $\Gamma_3$, the loci of inlet conditions, can be found by integrating back along adiabatics until $J(c_3,T_3)$ is zero or $2\mu/\lambda$. Proceeding in this way families of curves $\Gamma_1', \ldots \Gamma_R'$ and $\Gamma_1, \ldots \Gamma_R$ (with two branches each, $\Gamma_{1*}, \Gamma_1^*, \ldots, \Gamma_R^*$) can be drawn. For an $R$-bed design generally only the branch $\Gamma_{R*}$ of $\Gamma_R$, and the branches $\Gamma_r^*$ of $\Gamma_r$, $r = (R - 1), \ldots 1$, will be needed

of the second family. The optimal design is then given by an alternation of horizontal lines and lines of slope $H$ passing from the feed state $(c'_{R+1}, T'_{R+1})$ to $\Gamma_{R*}$ and on to $\Gamma'_R, \Gamma^*_{R-1}, \Gamma'_{R-1}, \Gamma^*_{R-2}, \ldots, \Gamma^*_1, \Gamma'_1$ in succession.

The presentation of this case has been dominated by the graphical construction that is possible, for it is felt that this provides a rapid solution of sufficient accuracy for preliminary design discussions. The actual details of the calculation are of course most expeditiously performed on a digital computer. Here the loci, $\Gamma$, would be stored as tables and used as such and for any given values of $\lambda$ and $\mu$ the whole process would be a matter of minutes. We shall now show how the availability of solutions of this simple model allows us to solve other significant design problems.

## 6.2. Extended Results of the Simple Model

The constants $\lambda$ and $\mu$ may be regarded as Lagrange multipliers, and we could write

$$\text{Max } P_R = qv f_R(c'_{R+1}, T'_{R+1}; \lambda, \mu). \tag{1}$$

Suppose now that we ask for an optimal design that will have a total bed volume of $V$. Since $V = q \sum_1^R \theta_r$ it can be calculated from the optimal policy for any given $\lambda$ and $q$. Now $\Theta_R(\lambda) = \sum_1^R \theta_r$ is a function of $\lambda$ independent of $q$, so that if $q$ is fixed by some other consideration the problem is solved by (1) with the value of $\lambda$ that gives $\Theta_R(\lambda) = V/q$. There are situations where this consideration is of overriding importance, as for example in high-pressure technology where an existing forging may be too valuable to be discarded but the converter within it needs to be redesigned. A similar use could be made of $\mu$ if it were required to limit the total heat interchange.

An interesting consideration arises when a fixed production of one chemical species, say $A_1$, is required. The rate at which $A_1$ is being formed is $q\alpha_1(c'_1 - c'_{R+1})$, so that for any given $q$ the exit extent $c'_1$ is fixed. Suppose that $\mu$ is known and either $\lambda$ or $V$ is given: in the latter case $\lambda$ is determined for any $q$ as above. We now work backwards from the end, for the exit conditions must lie on $\Gamma'_1$ where $c = c'_1$. Then proceeding successively to $\Gamma^*_1, \Gamma'_2, \Gamma^*_2$, etc., by adiabatic or horizontal lines we shall eventually reach the line $c = c'_{R+1}$. The point at which this is reached, however, is not necessarily an optimal

117

inlet temperature, but the total profit $P_R$ can be calculated. It will be a function of $q$ and a few repetitions of this calculation will suffice to determine it. If $h(q)$ represents the pumping costs the best design will be the one that maximizes $P_R - h(q)$. In this way the number of beds has also been determined, and if the restriction on $V$ has been used their total volume will be constant. It should be noted that this calculation is a direct one, for the fixing of $c_1'$ fixes also $T_1'$ as the higher temperature at which $r(c_1',T_1') = \lambda$. The integral $J$ is now calculated down the adiabatic from this point until it is $-\mu/\lambda$; this determines $c_1,T_1$. Now $c$ is held constant and $r(c_1,T)$ calculated until its value again drops to $r(c_1,T_1)$. Then $J$ is calculated down the adiabatic until it is zero and so on until $c = c_{R+1}'$.

If a more general valuation of the stream is used, say

$$v(c) = v(c_{10} + \alpha_1 c, \ldots c_{n0} + \alpha_n c),$$

and $v$ is differentiable, the same method works. We replace $I$ by the integral

$$\int_c^{c'} \left\{ v'(c) - \frac{\lambda}{r(c,T)} \right\} dc.$$

The curve $\Gamma_1'$ is now the locus on which

$$v'(c)r(c,T) = \lambda$$

but from this point onwards the construction goes through as before.

## 6.3. Interchanger Cooling with Simultaneous Reactions

If $t$ is again the holding time from the beginning of the bed, the equations for $m$ simultaneous reactions are obtained from (3.4.11) and (3.4.12) by setting $Q' = 0$:

$$\frac{dc^j}{dt} = r^j(c^1, \ldots c^m, T),$$

$$j = 1, \ldots m, \qquad (1)$$

$$\frac{dT}{dt} = \sum_{j=1}^m H^j r^j(c^1, \ldots c^m, T). \qquad (2)$$

By eliminating the $r^j$ between Eqs. (1) and (2) it follows that

$$T = T_i + \sum_{j=1}^m H^j(c^j - c_i^j), \qquad (3)$$

118

where $c_i^1, \ldots c_i^m, T_i$ is the state at any point in the bed. Equation (3) may be substituted in Eqs. (1) to make them a complete set of $m$ equations that can be integrated together. However, with high-speed computation there is probably little need to do this.

As before, we use a prime to denote conditions at the exit of the bed and a suffix $r$ to denote values appropriate to bed $r$. It will then be possible by integrating Eqs. (1) and (2) to determine the exit conditions in terms of the inlet conditions and $\theta_r$. This process will usually be a matter of numerical computation, but we may express the fact that it can be done by writing

$$c_r^{j'} = c_r^j + h_j(c_r^1, \ldots c_r^m, T_r, \theta_r)$$

$$j = 1, \ldots m, \qquad (4)$$

$$T_r' = T_r + \sum_1^m H^j h_j(c_r^1, \ldots c_r^m, T_r, \theta_r). \qquad (5)$$

Since there is no reaction in the interchanger,

$$c_{r+1}^{j'} = c_r^j. \qquad (6)$$

Let $v(c^1, \ldots c^m)$ denote the value of a unit volume of the process stream when the extents of reaction are $c^1, \ldots c^m$; then the total gain in value through the reactor is

$$q\{v(c_1^{1'}, \ldots c_1^{m'}) - v(c_{R+1}^1, \ldots c_{R+1}^m)\}$$

$$= q \sum_1^R \{v(c_r^{1'}, \ldots c_r^{m'}) - v(c_r^1, \ldots c_r^m)\}. \qquad (7)$$

The costs associated with the reactor are:

$C_1(\theta_r, q)$, the amortized construction and maintenance cost of a bed of holding time $\theta_r$ when the flow rate is $q$;

$C_2(T_{r+1}', T_r, q)$, the cost of construction and maintenance of interchanger for the duty of removing or adding heat to the stream of flow rate $q$ so as to change its temperature from $T_{r+1}'$ to $T_r$;[†]

$C_3(q)$, the cost of pumping the process stream. This term may be a function not only of $q$ but also of the whole design. However, as $q$ does not vary from stage to stage but must be held constant for all, this could be taken into account.

---

[†] If heat is being removed an interchanger may be used, but if it is being added this may have to be done by a furnace or electrical heater. Thus $C_2$ may be very different when $T_{r+1}' < T_r$ from what it is when $T_r < T_{r+1}'$.

## 6. THE MULTIBED ADIABATIC REACTOR

Thus the objective function which expresses the net profit from the reactor is

$$P_R = q \sum_1^R \{v(c_r^{k'}) - v(c_r^k)\} - \sum_1^R C_1(\theta_r, q) - \sum_1^R C_2(T'_{r+1}, T_r, q) - C_3(q)$$

(8)

Since $q$ does not vary from stage to stage we must hold it constant during the dynamic programming. Let

$$\frac{\{P_R + C_3(q)\}}{q} = \sum_1^R p_r$$

(9)

where

$$p_r = v(c_r^{k'}) - v(c_r^k) - \gamma_1(\theta_r) - \gamma_2(T'_{r+1}, T_r),$$

(10)

and

$$\gamma_1(\theta_r) = C_1(\theta_r, q)/q$$

$$\gamma_2(T'_{r+1}, T_r) = C_2(T'_{r+1}, T_r, q)/q.$$

(11)

Now let

$$f_R(c_{R+1}^{k'}, T'_{R+1}) = \text{Max} \sum_1^R p_r.$$

(12)

Then the principle of optimality gives

$$f_R(c_{R+1}^{k'}, T'_{R+1}) = \text{Max} \{p_R + f_{R-1}(c_R^{k'}, T'_R)\}.$$

(13)

In this last maximization we have only to choose $T_R$ and $\theta_R$, for then the whole expression is calculable by means of (4) and (5).

The solution of this equation is difficult only in that a function of $m + 1$ variables has to be stored and interpolated. If this is possible the maximization may be performed straightforwardly. For any trial value of $T_R$ the integration of Eqs. (1) and (2) is carried out until the maximum of $p_R + f_{R-1}$ is reached. This is when

$$\sum_{j=1}^m \left\{ \frac{\partial v}{\partial c^{j'}} + \frac{\partial f_{R-1}}{\partial c^{j'}} + H^j \frac{\partial f_{R-1}}{\partial T'} \right\} r^j(c_r^{k'}, T_r) = \gamma_1'(\theta_r)$$

(14)

and only in the special case $\gamma_1' = \text{constant}$ does this define a unique point on the adiabatic path. The resultant maximum of $p_R + f_{R-1}$ is recorded and the calculation repeated for a new $T_R$ until the optimal value of this is also found.

This whole process is done for a constant $q$, and for this value of $q$

$$\text{Max } P_R = q f_R - C_3(q).$$

Again, it may happen that there is an optimal value of $q$ and this

120

must be found by a further maximization with respect to variations of $q$.

If $m > 2$ the whole method very definitely falls under "the curse of dimensionality" and there seems no way of escape. However, in many situations it is possible to consider only one dominant and one side reaction. This should at least give some idea of where the optimal policy lies and if necessary could be used to determine comparatively small regions within which $f_1, f_2, \ldots f_{R-1}$ would be needed later for interpolation.

## 6.4. *Cold Shot Cooling with a Single Reaction*

In discussing the cold shot cooling we will introduce a slight change of variable. This could have been done before and is not necessary now, but we do it to exhibit a form which may appeal to some readers as slightly more elegant. Let us denote by $c_0, T_0$ the state of the cold unreacted feed which is to be used both for the cold shot cooling and, after heating, for the feed to the first bed. We can without loss of generality put $c_0 = 0$, and in place of $T$ we take

$$t = (T - T_0)/H. \tag{1}$$

Thus the feed stock is represented by the origin in the $c,t$ plane and Eq. (6.1.2) for an adiabatic reaction path becomes

$$t = t_i + c - c_i. \tag{2}$$

The transformation is really a normalization of the $c,T$ plane to bring the origin to the state of the basic feed and make the adiabatic lines of unit slope.

The system of beds is entirely similar to that of the stirred tanks shown in Fig. 5.18. A fraction $\lambda_R q$ of the initial flow is preheated and passed to the reactor $R$, and the rest is split between the beds. $\lambda_r q$ is the flow through reactor $r$ whose inlet and exit conditions are denoted by $c_r, t_r$ and $c'_r, t'_r$ respectively. It follows from the simple expressions for mixing that

$$\lambda_r c_r = \lambda_{r+1} c'_{r+1} \quad \text{and} \quad \lambda_r t_r = \lambda_{r+1} t'_{r+1} \tag{3}$$

and it is convenient to introduce, as before,

$$\mu_{r+1} = \lambda_{r+1}/\lambda_r \tag{4}$$

so that

$$c_r = \mu_{r+1} c'_{r+1}, \qquad t_r = \mu_{r+1} t'_{r+1}. \tag{5}$$

For a bed of volume $V_r$

$$\frac{V_r}{q\lambda_r} = \int_{c_r}^{c'_r} \frac{dc}{r(c, c + t_r - c_r)} \tag{6}$$

and it is convenient to take the holding time $\theta_r = V_r/q$ to be the mean residence time if the whole flow were through the bed.

As before, we are concerned to maximize the final extent of reaction $c'_1$ and since $\lambda_1 = 1$, $c_R = c_0 = 0$ we can write this

$$c'_1 = \sum_{r=1}^{R} \lambda_r(c'_r - c_r) \tag{7}$$

by virtue of Eqs. (3). If the cost of the bed is again proportional to its volume we can write a suitable objective function in the form

$$P_R = \sum_{1}^{R} p_r = \sum_{1}^{R} \lambda_r(c'_r - c_r) - v\theta_r$$

$$= \sum_{1}^{R} \lambda_r \int_{c_r}^{c'_r} \left\{ 1 - \frac{v}{r_r(c)} \right\} dc. \tag{8}$$

This maximization has to be attained by choosing the $R$ bed sizes, $\theta_R, \ldots \theta_1$, the $(R - 1)$ bypass rates $\lambda_R, \ldots \lambda_2$, and the inlet temperature $t_R$. An equivalent set of choices, and one which the form of the equations makes more convenient, is that of $t_R, \lambda_R, \ldots \lambda_2$, $c'_R, \ldots c'_1$. The objective function (8) considers only the net gain from the adiabatic part of the system, and in choosing $t_R$ we shall have to bring in a cost of preheating. However, it is necessary to treat the last $(R - 1)$ beds separately in much the same way as was done for the stirred tank sequence. This is because bed $R$ is on a slightly different basis; it must be considered together with the preheater just as the others are considered together with their pre-mixing devices.

Let

$$f_{R-1}(c'_R, t'_R) = \text{Maximum value of } P_{R-1} \text{ when the exit}$$
$$\text{state from reactor } R \text{ is } c'_R, t'_R.$$

Then by the principle of optimality

$$f_{R-1}(c'_R, t'_R) = \text{Max} \left[ \lambda_{R-1} \int_{c_{R-1}}^{c'_{R-1}} \left\{ 1 - \frac{v}{r_{R-1}(c)} \right\} dc + f_{R-2}(c'_{R-1}, t'_{R-1}) \right] \tag{9}$$

122

where

$$c_{R-1} = \mu_R c_R'$$

and the maximum is to be attained by choice of $\mu_R$ and $c_{R-1}'$.

We look again at the situation for one adiabatic bed $(R = 2)$,

$$f_1(c_2', t_2') = \text{Max} \int_{c_1}^{c_1'} \left\{ 1 - \frac{\nu}{r_1(c)} \right\} dc, \tag{10}$$

and

$$c_1 = \mu_2 c_2', \qquad t_1 = \mu_2 t_2'.$$

The choice of $c_1'$ is made as before by observing that if $\mu_2$ has been chosen the vanishing of the derivative of the right-hand side of (10) requires that

$$r(c_1', t_1') = \nu. \tag{11}$$

Hence as before we have a locus $\Gamma_1'$ on which the exit conditions must lie. To find the optimal value of $\mu_2$ it is best to proceed by direct calculation, for in this case analytical relationships do not simplify as before. The point $(c_1, t_1)$ always lies on the ray through the origin and the given $(c_2', t_2')$. We therefore pick any point on this line and integrate along the adiabatic to $\Gamma_1'$ to calculate $p_1$. By selecting that starting point which gives the greatest value we have the value of $\mu_2$ from the ratio $c_1/c_2'$. It is evident that this optimal inlet condition is the same for all points $c_2', t_2'$ which are on the same ray through the origin. We can repeat this calculation with different rays, i.e., different values of $t_2'/c_2'$, and so develop a locus of optimal inlet conditions $\Gamma_1$. Then $f_1(c_2', t_2')$ is identically zero to the left of $\Gamma_1$ while to the right of it $f_1$ is a function only of the ratio $\tau_2 = c_2'/t_2'$. This is confirmed by the analytical condition for $\Gamma_1$, namely,

$$\frac{\nu(1 - \tau_2)}{\tau_2} = 1 - \frac{[\nu/r(c_1, t_1)]}{J_1(c_1, t_1)} \tag{12}$$

giving

$$f_1(c_2', t_2') = \phi_1(\tau_2) = \int_{c_1}^{c_1'} \left\{ 1 - \frac{\nu}{r(c, c + t_1(1 - \tau_2))} \right\} dc. \tag{13}$$

The fact that $f_1$ is really only a function of one variable and that this variable lies in the range $(0,1)$ makes storage and interpolation a simple matter. The next step is also best performed by direct search:

$$f_2(c_3', t_3') = \text{Max} \left[ \lambda_2 \int_{c_2}^{c_2'} \left\{ 1 - \frac{\nu}{r_2(c)} \right\} dc + \phi_1\left( \frac{c_2'}{t_2'} \right) \right]. \tag{14}$$

123

Taking any point on the line $c = \tau_3 t$, $\tau_3 = c_3'/t_3'$, the expression to be maximized can be calculated along the adiabatic through this point until its maximum is reached. This is possible since $\lambda_2 \doteq \mu_2$ is known from the one-stage policy. This maximum is recorded and by comparison of successive trials starting with points along the ray the optimal inlet conditions $(c_2, t_2)$ and the consequent outlet conditions $(c_2', t_2')$ can be found. Repeating this for various $\tau_3$ allows the loci $\Gamma_2$ and $\Gamma_2'$ to be constructed. Figure 6.8 illustrates this and

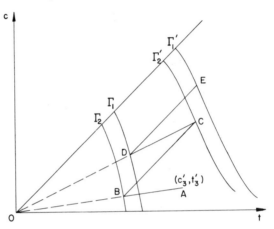

FIG. 6.8. The optimal cold shot design for two beds.

shows how the optimal policy for any $(c_3', t_3')$ can be constructed. The values of $\lambda_2$ and $\lambda_3$ are found from the ratios $\mu_2 = OD/OC$, $\mu_3 = OB/OA$, whence $\lambda_2 = \mu_2$, $\lambda_3 = \mu_3\mu_2$. The curves $\Gamma_1$ and $\Gamma_2$ could readily be graduated in $f_1$ and $f_2$ and $\Gamma_1', \Gamma_2'$ in $\theta_1$ and $\theta_2$ and then the complete optimal policy could be read off. This construction is continued to $\Gamma_{R-1}$ and $\Gamma_{R-1}'$.

For the first stage and its preheater we have to take into account the cost $h(t_R)$ of heating the feed to a temperature $t_R$. We maximize

$$\lambda_R \int_0^{c'_R} \left\{1 - \frac{\nu}{r(c, c + t_R)}\right\} dc - h(t_R) + f_{R-1}(c_R', t_R') \tag{15}$$

by choice of $c_R'$ and $t_R$. If $h(t)$ is a fixed function this gives us a unique design. If $h(t, \alpha)$ is a family of functions depending on a cost parameter $\alpha$, then $t_R$ and $c_R'$ will be functions of $\alpha$. The $t$ axis can be graduated in $\alpha$ and a locus $\Gamma_R'$ of exit conditions can be drawn, and so an immediate design is made available for any $\alpha$.

124

The extensions of this model to problems requiring a given total volume or a given production can be made in the same way as before. It is evident that there is a limitation present with cold shot converters which does not apply to the interchanger type, for no adiabatic line can rise above the line of unit slope through the origin. Hence the greatest conversion attainable is the equilibrium conversion that would be achieved if the feed were passed to a single adiabatic bed of infinite length.

## 6.5. *Cold Shot Cooling with Simultaneous Reactions*

In discussing the general algorithm for a cold shot reactor with $m$ simultaneous reactions we will return to the extent variables $c^j$ and actual temperature $T$. Let $c_0^j$ and $T_0$ denote the state of the cold unreacted feed and $q_r$ be the flow rate of reactants through the bed $r$ of volume $V_r$. The bypass that is mixed with the process stream between beds $(r+1)$ and $r$ is $(q_r - q_{r-1})$ so that mass and heat balances give

$$q_r c_r^j = q_{r+1} c_{r+1}^{j'} + (q_r - q_{r+1}) c_0^j,$$
$$j = 1, \ldots m, \qquad (1)$$
$$q_r T_r = q_{r+1} T_{r+1}' + (q_r - q_{r+1}) T_0. \qquad (2)$$

As before, the solutions of the governing equations (6.3.1) and (6.3.2) can be expressed in the form

$$c_r^{j'} = c_r^j + h_j(c_r^1, \ldots c_r^m, T_r, V_r/q_r) \qquad (3)$$

$$T_r' = T_r + \sum_1^R H^j h_j(c_r^1, \ldots c_r^m, T_r, V_r/q_r). \qquad (4)$$

The objective function is constructed as before using a value function in terms of the extents and the following costs:

$C_1(V_r, q_r)$, the amortized construction and maintenance cost of a bed of volume $V_r$ with flow rate $q_r$;

$C_2(q_r, q_{r+1})$, the cost of constructing and maintaining a mixing chamber that will take two flows of rate $q_{r+1}$ and $(q_r - q_{r+1})$ and mix them satisfactorily. This term should also include the incremental pumping cost for the bypass flow rate;

$C_3(T_R, T_0, q_R)$, the cost of pumping the feed at rate $q_R$ and heating it from temperature $T_0$ to $T_R$.

## 6. THE MULTIBED ADIABATIC REACTOR

Then the full objective function is

$$P_R = q_1\{v(c_1^{k'}) - v(c_0^k)\} - \sum_1^R C_1(V_r, q_r)$$
$$- \sum_1^{R-1} C_2(q_r, q_{r+1}) - C_3(T_R, T_0, q_R). \tag{5}$$

This we will write in the form

$$P_R = \sum_1^{R-1} p_r + \{q_r \bar{v}(c_R') - C_1(V_R, q_R) - C_3(T_R, T_0, q_R)\} \tag{6}$$

where

$$p_r = q_r \bar{v}(c_r') - q_{r+1}\bar{v}(c_{r+1}') - C_1(V_r, q_r) - C_2(q_r, q_{r+1}) \tag{7}$$

and

$$\bar{v}(c') = v(c^{1'}, \ldots c^{m'}) - v(c_0^1, \ldots c_0^m). \tag{8}$$

Again the direct application of dynamic programming is to the term $\sum p_r$, and the second term must be dealt with subsequently. Let

$$f_{R-1}(c_R^{k'}, T_R') = \text{Max} \sum_1^{R-1} p_r, \tag{9}$$

where the maximum is attained by the correct choice of variables $q_R, q_{R-1}, \ldots q_2$ and $V_{R-1}, \ldots V_1$. $q_1$, the total flow, is fixed, and the $q_r$ are subject to the restriction $q_R \leq q_{R-1} \leq \ldots \leq q_2 \leq q_1$. If $C_2(q_r, q_{r+1})$ were homogeneous of the first degree in $q_r$ and $q_{r+1}$ and $C_1$ were proportional to $q$, it would be possible to work only in the ratio $q_{r+1}/q_r = \mu_{r+1} < 1$, but we need not assume this to be the case. Application of the principle of optimality immediately gives

$$f_{R-1}(c_R^{k'}, T_R') = \text{Max}\{p_{R-1} + f_{R-2}(c_{R-1}^{k'}, T_{R-1}')\} \tag{10}$$

where the maximization is by suitable choice of $V_{R-1}$ and $q_R$. Since $q_{R-1}$ is known from the preceding solution of the equation, $p_{R-1}$ can be calculated for any value of $q_R$ and $V_{R-1}$. It is best to proceed sequentially, choosing a value of $q_R$ and fixing it while the best $V_{R-1}$ is found; this is then repeated until the best $q_R$ is also attained.

At the last stage we determine $T_R$ and $V_R$ so as to maximize

$$f_{R-1}(c_R^{k'}, T_R') + q_R \bar{v}(c_R') - C_1(V_R, q_R) - C_3(T_R, T_0, q_R). \tag{11}$$

This gives a complete design for an adiabatic reactor with $R$ beds, and as before the only real difficulty is in carrying along a function of $(m + 1)$ variables. With simple types of cost functions this may be reduced to an $m$-variable problem as in the previous paragraph, but no general escape from this difficulty seems possible.

126

## 6.6. *Cooling by an Alien Cold Shot*

Two compositions $c_i^1$ and $c_i^2$, $i = 1, \ldots n$, will be called alien if they cannot both arise from the same reference composition $c_{i0}$ by reaction to a certain extent. Thus two compositions are alien if $(c_i^1 - c_i^2)/\alpha_i$ is not independent of $i$ for a single reaction, and a more complicated relation holds for simultaneous reactions. We will consider the case where the source of supply for the cold shot is of an alien composition. This sometimes occurs in practice, as when air is used as the cold shot in the oxidation of sulfur dioxide.

Let $c_{i0}$ be the reference composition of the main supply of process stream and $\gamma_i$ that of the cold shot supply. Suppose a quantity of reactants of composition $c_i = c_{i0} + \alpha_i c$ is mixed with cold shot in the proportions $\lambda : (1 - \lambda)$. The resulting composition is

$$\lambda c_i + (1 - \lambda)\gamma_i = \{\lambda c_{i0} + (1 - \lambda)\gamma_i\} + \alpha_i \lambda c \qquad (1)$$

which is that of a mixture of reference composition $\lambda c_{i0} + (1 - \lambda)\gamma_i$ and extent of reaction $\lambda c$. Now the number of variables in $r(c_1, \ldots c_n, T)$ was reduced from $(n + 1)$ to two by substituting $c_i = c_{i0} + \alpha_i c$, and in doing so we implicitly carried along the reference composition $c_{i0}$. This is no longer fixed, so that now $r$ cannot be reduced to a function of only two variables. However the reference compositions now belong to a one-parameter family, $\lambda c_{i0} + (1 - \lambda)\gamma_i$, where this set of $c_{i0}$ and $\gamma_i$ are now fixed. We can thus write

$$
\begin{aligned}
r(c_1, \ldots c_n, T) &= r(\lambda c_{i0} + (1 - \lambda)\gamma_1 + \alpha_1 \lambda c, \ldots \\
&\qquad \lambda c_{n0} + (1 - \lambda)\gamma_n + \alpha_n \lambda c, T) \\
&= r(c, T, \lambda; c_{10}, \ldots c_{n0}; \gamma_1, \ldots \gamma_n) \\
&= r(c, T, \lambda) \qquad (2)
\end{aligned}
$$

and it appears that we can now get along with a function of three variables.

To see how $\lambda$ has to be chosen let us mix reactants with the composition (1) with more cold shot in the proportions $\mu : (1 - \mu)$. The resulting composition is

$$\mu\{\lambda c_i + (1 - \lambda)\gamma_i\} + (1 - \mu)\gamma_i = \{\mu\lambda c_{i0} + (1 - \mu\lambda)\gamma_i\} + \alpha_i \mu \lambda c \qquad (3)$$

which simply means that $\lambda$ is replaced by the resultant proportion

$\mu\lambda$ of the double mixing. On the other hand, suppose the composition (1) suffers reaction to a further extent $c'$ before mixing; then we have a composition

$$\{\mu\lambda c_{i0} + (1 - \mu\lambda)\gamma_i\} + \alpha_i(\mu\lambda c + \mu c'). \tag{4}$$

This has the same reference composition as (3) but an extent of reaction $\mu\lambda c + \mu c'$. It appears therefore that the reference composition changes only with the mixing. The extent changes only with the proportion of mixing that occurs after a given amount of reaction.

Thus a discussion of cooling with an alien cold shot would proceed on exactly the same lines as above, but would require functions of three variables for a single reaction, in place of the functions of two variables we have used above. For $m$ simultaneous reactions an entirely similar result holds, and these now demand functions of $(m + 2)$ variables.

## 6.7. *The Removal of Sundry Approximations*

We shall now indicate how several of the simplifying assumptions that have been made can be removed. To do so will involve a certain amount of extra work and it is necessary to decide whether the greater accuracy that is obtained is genuine or not. It is quite futile to compute the quotient of two numbers with two-figure accuracy to twenty places of decimals, for the last eighteen will be meaningless. In the same way a delicate consideration of the thermodynamics of mixing may be quite pedantic in the presence of considerable uncertainty in the kinetic constants. The following remarks are intended only to show how the assumptions could be lightened; they are not an exhortation to complication.

It was assumed earlier that the quotients of the heats of reaction and the specific heat were approximately constant. This is certainly unnecessary, for if $-\Delta H$ and $C_p$ are functions of composition and temperature we can write

$$-\Delta H/C_p = H(c_1, \ldots c_n, T) = H(c,T).$$

Now we have to solve simultaneously

$$\frac{dc}{dt} = r(c,T)$$

$$\frac{dT}{dt} = H(c,T)r(c,T),$$

but this presents no computational problems. If it is felt desirable, the adiabatic paths may be found first as solutions of the equation

$$\frac{dT}{dc} = H(c,T)$$

and these will replace the straight lines. In case $H(c,T) = H(T)$ is a function of temperature only, the new variable $t = \int^T d\tau/H(\tau)$ will have the same properties as in Section 6.4 and will make the adiabatic paths straight lines of unit slope. Similar results clearly hold for simultaneous reactions where in any case the equations cannot be solved by quadratures.

In cases where the pressure has an important effect it can be introduced as a new variable. It is calculated by using the full set of equations for the tubular reactor in place of the simplified set that we have taken. These have been given in Section 3.4.

Though comparatively little data is available, the heat of mixing is sometimes imported into discussions of reactor design.* It destroys the simplicity of such equations as (6.4.3) and (6.5.2), but aside from replacing them with formidable formulas of supernal sophistication, it introduces nothing that the method cannot handle. Thus when data is available and the effect is deemed to be significant it can be taken into account. When data is neither available nor easily obtainable it affords the defaulting designer an impregnable alibi.

---

* This is a valuable item in the academic and industrial technologist's repertoire of gambits. For further details see Potter (1951).

# 7

# The Tubular Reactor

---

*For the Snark's a peculiar creature, that won't*
  *Be caught in a commonplace way.*
*Do all that you know and try all that you don't:*
  *Not a chance must be wasted today!*

---

In this chapter we pass from the discrete to the continuous deterministic process, and the difference equations derived for the stages now become differential equations. It is scarcely surprising to find many features of the discrete process are retained by the continuous process: in particular we know from the work of Denbigh (1944), and will prove here afresh, that the optimal temperature policy is disjoint in the case of a single reaction. However, this simplicity is lost when more than one reaction is taking place and we shall do well to examine the simple consecutive system $A \to B \to C$ with some care, as it opens up the principal features of the general case.

It should not be forgotten that all the examples of this chapter are patient of two interpretations, for the same equations apply to both tubular and batch reactors. Indeed, as we shall see in the final chapter, when considering control, it is perhaps easier to attain the optimal conditions in the batch reactor. For definiteness however it will be convenient to speak in terms of the tubular reactor.

# 7.1. Optimal Temperature Policy with a Single Reaction

For a single reaction whose progress is measured by the extent $c$, the simplest equations of the tubular reactor are (3.4.13) and (3.4.14):

$$\frac{dc}{dt} = -r(c,T) \tag{1}$$

$$\frac{dT}{dt} = -Hr(c,T) + Q. \tag{2}$$

Here $t$ is the holding time measured from the end of the reactor (or time from the end of a batch reaction) and $Q$ is proportional to the rate of heat removal per unit length (or unit time). We address first the problem of determining the optimal temperature gradient when no account is taken of the cost of attaining this optimum. This requires only the consideration of Eq. (1) to give the optimal policy $T(t)$ or $T(c)$. The variation of $Q$ required to bring this about is then given by Eq. (2):

$$Q = \frac{d}{dt}(T - Hc). \tag{3}$$

We shall show that the temperature policy is disjoint in the sense that it is chosen to make the reaction rate as large as possible at each point.

Consider first the problem when the feed and product composition are both fixed and it is required to obtain this conversion in the least possible time. The product, or exit, composition being fixed, $c(0) = c_e$, we recognize that, when the optimal policy is used, the holding time required will be a function only of the feed composition, $c(\theta) = c_f$. We may write

$$f(c_f) = \text{Min } \theta = \text{Min} \int_{c_e}^{c_f} \frac{dc}{-r(c,T)}$$

$$= \text{Min} \int_{c_f}^{c_e} \frac{dc}{r(c,T)} \tag{4}$$

where the minimization is by correct choice of $T$ as a function of $c$, $c_f \leq c \leq c_e$, in the interval

$$T_* \leq T \leq T^*. \tag{5}$$

## 7.1. OPTIMAL TEMPERATURE POLICY WITH A SINGLE REACTION

Now let $\gamma$ be a small positive quantity less than $(c_e - c_f)$; then

$$\int_{c_f}^{c_e} \frac{dc}{r(c,T)} = \int_{c_f}^{c_f+\gamma} \frac{dc}{r(c,T)} + \int_{c_f+\gamma}^{c_e} \frac{dc}{r(c,T)}$$

and the second of these integrals is the time required to reach the required product composition from the feed state $c_f + \gamma$. Since, by the principle of optimality, this section should be using the optimal policy,

$$f(c_f) = \text{Min}\left[\int_{c_f}^{c_f+\gamma} \frac{dc}{r(c,T)} + f(c_f + \gamma)\right], \tag{6}$$

where the minimization is by choice of $T(c)$ for $c_f \le c \le c_f + \gamma$. Since this is true for all $\gamma$ we may let $\gamma \to 0$, obtaining for small $\gamma$

$$f(c_f) = \text{Min}\left[\frac{\gamma}{r(c,T)} + f(c_f) + \gamma f'(c_f) + 0(\gamma^2)\right]$$

and hence

$$-f'(c_f) = \text{Min} \frac{1}{r(c_f,T_f)} \tag{7}$$

where $T_f = T(c_f) = T(\theta)$. But Eq. (7) shows immediately that $T$ should be chosen so that $r$ is as large as possible. Let

$$R(c) = \text{Max } r(c,T), \qquad T_* \le T \le T^* \tag{8}$$

then

$$-f'(c_f) = 1/R(c_f)$$

or

$$f(c_f) = \int_{c_f}^{c_e} \frac{dc}{R(c)}. \tag{9}$$

We have already seen in Chapter 5 that an explicit expression can be found for $R(c)$ when the homogeneous kinetic law

$$r(c,T) = k_1(T) \prod_1^n (c_{i0} + \alpha_i c)^{\beta_i} - k_2(T) \prod_1^n (c_{i0} + \alpha_i c)^{\gamma_i} \tag{10}$$

expresses the rate of the reaction $\sum \alpha_i A_i = 0$. This is

$$R(c) = \frac{p^p}{(p+1)^{p+1}} \frac{k_1^{*p+1}}{k_2^{*p}} \prod_1^n (c_{i0} + \alpha_i c)^{\beta_i - p\alpha_i} \tag{11}$$

where

$$p = E_1/(E_2 - E_1)$$

and

$$k_i = k_i^* \exp\{-E_i/RT\}, \qquad i = 1,2.$$

133

The corresponding value of the optimal temperature is

$$T = \frac{E_2 - E_1}{R} \left[ \ln \frac{k_2^* E_2}{k_1^* E_1} \prod_1^n (c_{i0} + \alpha_i c)^{\alpha_i} \right]^{-1}. \tag{12}$$

This may be put into dimensionless form by making the following abbreviations:

$$c_0 = \sum_1^n c_{i0}, \quad \mu_i = c_{i0}/c_0, \quad x = c/c_0,$$

$$\alpha = \sum_1^n \alpha_i, \quad \beta = \sum_1^n \beta_i, \quad \gamma = \sum_1^n \gamma_i,$$

$$\delta_i = p\alpha_i - \beta_i = (E_1\gamma_i - E_2\beta_i)/(E_2 - E_1) \tag{13}$$

$$A = \frac{p^p}{(p+1)^{p+1}} \frac{k_1^{*p+1}}{k_2^{*p}} c_0^{(p+1)\beta - p\gamma - 1}.$$

Then

$$R(c) = c_0 A P(x)$$

$$P(x) = \prod_1^n (\mu_i + \alpha_i x)^{-\delta_i} \tag{14}$$

and $P$ is dimensionless since $A$ has the dimensions of $(\text{time})^{-1}$. The dimensionless temperature $\tau$ is

$$\tau = \frac{RT}{E_2 - E_1} = \left[ \ln \kappa \prod_1^n (\mu_i + \alpha_i x)^{\alpha_i} \right]^{-1} \tag{15}$$

where

$$\kappa = \frac{p+1}{p} \frac{k_2^*}{k_1^*} c_0^\alpha. \tag{16}$$

When Eq. (9) is cast into this form we have

$$Af(c_f) = \int_{x_f}^{x_e} \prod_1^n (\mu_i + \alpha_i x)^{\delta_i} \, dx \tag{17}$$

where $x_f = c_f/\sum c_{i0}$, $x_e = c_e/\sum c_{i0}$. We observe that $\delta_i$ is generally negative for species being used up in the reaction and positive for those being formed. The integral will therefore diverge as $x$ approaches the least positive value of $-\mu_i/\alpha_i$, i.e., one of the species becomes completely used up. Such an integral as (17) is very readily computed as

$$F(x) = \int_0^x \prod_1^n (\mu_i + \alpha_i x)^{\delta_i} \, dx. \tag{18}$$

Then the dimensionless minimum holding time $Af(c_f)$ is given by

$$Af(c_f) = F(x_e) - F(x_f). \tag{19}$$

In this form it appears that the problem can be solved for all $x_e$ and does not need to be started afresh if a different $x_e$ is required. This is a happy consequence of the disjointness of the policy.

Two remarks should be added before giving an illustration. Firstly, the above analysis is interesting only for exothermic reactions $E_2 > E_1$, for the maximum rate of an endothermic reaction is always at the highest permissible temperature. This is clear from Eq. (10), for (with an obvious abbreviation)

$$r = k_1\Pi_1 - k_2\Pi_2$$

whence

$$\frac{\partial r}{\partial T} = \frac{1}{RT^2}(k_1 E_1 \Pi_1 - k_2 E_2 \Pi_2).$$

Now if $r$ is positive, $k_1\Pi_1 > k_2\Pi_2$ and so $\partial r/\partial T$ is also positive if $E_1 > E_2$. The same expression shows that the extremum given by $\partial r/\partial T = 0$ for an exothermic reaction $(E_2 > E_1)$ is a maximum; for if $r > 0$ and $\partial r/\partial T = 0$

$$\frac{\partial^2 r}{\partial T^2} = \frac{1}{R^2 T^4}(k_1 E_1^2 \Pi_1 - k_2 E_2^2 \Pi_2)$$

is certainly negative. Secondly we should notice that for an exothermic reaction the optimal temperature is a monotonic decreasing function of the extent, for differentiating (15) we have

$$\frac{d\tau}{dx} = -\tau^2 \sum_1^n \frac{\alpha_i^2}{(\mu_i + \alpha_i x)}.$$

It follows that there is an interval $(x_*, x^*)$ within which the optimal temperature is given by (15). Outside this interval we have $\tau = \tau^* = RT^*/(E_2 - E_1)$ for $x < x_*$, $\tau = \tau_* = RT_*/(E_2 - E_1)$ for $x > x^*$. $x_*$ and $x^*$ are the values of $x$ that make $\tau = \tau^*$ and $\tau_*$ respectively in Eq. (15). Thus outside this interval the dimensionless reaction rate must be replaced by $P_*(x)$ or $P^*(x)$ in the intervals $x < x_*$ and $x > x^*$ respectively, where

$$P_*(x) = \frac{k_1(T^*)c_0^{\beta-1}}{A} \prod_1^n (\mu_i + \alpha_i x)^{\beta_i} - \frac{k_2(T^*)c_0^{\gamma-1}}{A} \prod_1^n (\mu_i + \alpha_i x)^{\gamma_i} \tag{20}$$

and $P^*(x)$ is the same expression but with $k_1$ and $k_2$ evaluated at $T_*$. The integration of the reciprocal of either of these expressions is again a straightforward matter and if we define

$$F_*(x) = \int_0^x \frac{dx}{P_*(x)}, \qquad F^*(x) = \int_0^x \frac{dx}{P^*(x)} \tag{21}$$

and

$$\mathfrak{F}(x) = \begin{cases} F_*(x), & x < x_*, \\ F_*(x_*) - F(x_*) + F(x), & x_* \le x \le x^*, \\ F_*(x_*) - F(x_*) + F(x^*) - F^*(x^*) + F^*(x), & x \ge x^*, \end{cases} \tag{22}$$

then Eq. (19) holds in the form

$$Af(c_f) = \mathfrak{F}(x_e) - \mathfrak{F}(x_f). \tag{23}$$

This analysis has incidentally shown that $(2n + 3)$ parameters are involved in the study of a single reaction $\sum \alpha_i A_i = 0$ between $n$ species for which the rate law (10) is valid. These are

(i) the $n$ values of the order constants $\beta_i$, for the $\gamma_i$ are fixed by consistency with equilibrium ($\gamma_i = \alpha_i + \beta_i$);

(ii) the ratio of activation energies $(p + 1)/p$;

(iii) $\kappa$, the constant fixing the optimal temperature;

(iv) the $(n - 1)$ constants $\mu_i$ fixing the proportions of the reference composition;

(v) the bounds on the temperature, $\tau_*$ and $\tau^*$.

The constant $A$ is used to render the time dimensionless. In case the kinetic constants $\beta_i$ are fixed and we consider only one reference composition, there are only two parameters $p$ and $\kappa$ and these are separated in the sense that $p$ is associated with the integral $F$ whilst $\kappa$ is associated with the temperature policy.

In the case of a reversible first-order reaction $A_1 - A_2 = 0$ we have by this title fixed the constants $\beta_2 = \gamma_1 = 1$, $\beta_1 = \gamma_2 = 0$ and since all compositions can be obtained from pure $A_2$ we lose no generality by taking $\mu_1 = 0$, $\mu_2 = 1$. Thus we have $x = c/c_{20}$,

$$r(c,T) = k_1(T)(1 - x) - k_2(T)x \tag{24}$$

and

$$P(x) = x^{-p}(1 - x)^{p+1} \tag{25}$$

$$\tau = [\ln \kappa x/(1 - x)]^{-1}. \tag{26}$$

The function

$$z(x) = \int_0^x x^p(1 - x)^{-p-1}\, dx \tag{27}$$

is shown in Fig. 7.1 for several values of $p$, while in Fig. 7.2 the behavior of $\tau$ is given for various $\kappa$. These may be used as follows.

136

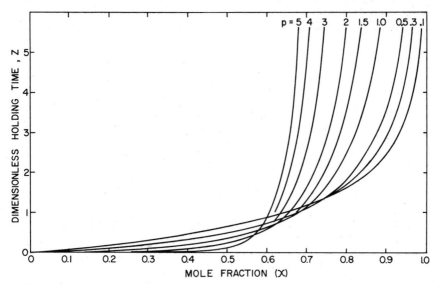

FIG. 7.1. Optimal reactor length as a function of composition for a first order reversible reaction.

In the lower part of Fig. 7.3 the $\tau - x$ curve for the appropriate $\kappa$ is drawn. If $\tau_*$ and $\tau^*$ are the bounds on the dimensionless temperature we immediately see that the segment AC of the curve is the only part needed and we have determined $x_*$ and $x^*$. In the upper

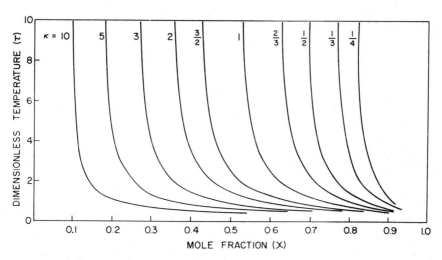

FIG. 7.2. Optimal temperature for a first order reaction.

137

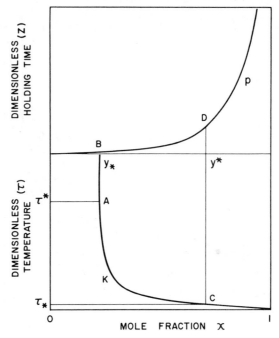

FIG. 7.3. The determination of the optimal temperature gradient.

part of the figure is the appropriate curve of $z(x)$ and of this the segment BD is all that is appropriate. Within this segment $z$ is determined as a function of $x$ and so $\tau$ as a function of $z$. If the value of $x_f$ should be less than $x_*$, then $z$ can be calculated from the integral of (24), namely:

$$A\theta - z(x) = \frac{1}{k_1 + k_2} \ln \frac{k_1 - (k_1 + k_2)x_f}{k_1 - (k_1 + k_2)x} \tag{28}$$

with $k_1$ and $k_2$ evaluated at $T = T^*$; $z = A\theta$ when $x = x_f$. Thus $z^*$, the point at which the falling temperature gradient starts, is

$$A\theta - z^* = \frac{1}{k_1 + k_2} \ln \frac{k_1 - (k_1 + k_2)x_f}{k_1 - (k_1 + k_2)x_*}. \tag{29}$$

From this point on the curve BD is used, until if $x_e > x^*$ the integrated form

$$z = \frac{1}{k_1 + k_2} \ln \frac{k_1 - (k_1 + k_2)x}{k_1 - (k_1 + k_2)x_e} \tag{30}$$

is used (here $k_1$ and $k_2$ are evaluated at $T = T_*$); $x = x_e$ when $z = 0$.

138

From (30) the point at which the final policy $T = T_*$ begins is

$$z_* = \frac{1}{k_1 + k_2} \ln \frac{k_1 - (k_1 + k_2)x^*}{k_1 - (k_1 + k_2)x_e}, \tag{31}$$

and the value of $\theta$ comes from the fact that

$$z^* - z_* = \int_{x_*}^{x^*} x^p(1 - x)^{-p-1} \, dx. \tag{32}$$

Figure 7.4 shows the resulting temperature profile.

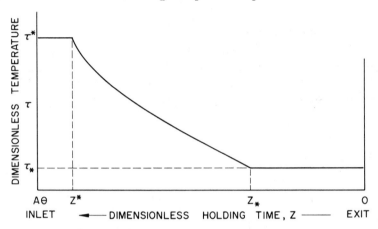

Fig. 7.4. The optimal temperature gradient.

A practical application of such a parametric study might be the determination of optimal conditions for a particular batch of catalyst. For example the Temkin equation, which is of the form (10), is used with some confidence for the ammonia synthesis reaction (Annable, 1952). However, the values of the constants $k_1^*$, $k_2^*$, $E_1$, and $E_2$ may vary with different catalysts and so the constants $p$, $\kappa$, and $A$ and the consequent optimal policy. As we shall now show the results of this section could be used to determine the maximum conversion from a fixed length of converter with the current brand of catalyst.

## 7.2. *Alternative Forms of the Optimal Problem with a Single Reaction*

It is instructive to approach the same problem from another angle and ask for the optimal temperature policy that will achieve the

139

greatest extent of reaction with a given holding time. Thus when $c(\theta) = c_f$ and $\theta$ are given we seek $T(t)$, $0 \leq t \leq \theta$ so that $c(0)$ is as large as possible. Let

$$f(c_f,\theta) = \text{Max} \{c(0) - c(\theta)\}$$

$$= \text{Max} \int_0^\theta \frac{dc}{dt} \, dt$$

$$= \text{Max} \int_0^\theta r(c,T) \, dt. \qquad (1)$$

Again we divide this integral into a short initial section $(\theta - \tau, \theta)$ followed by the remaining interval $(0, \theta - \tau)$ in which the principle of optimality forces the use of the optimal policy. Since the feed to this latter section has a composition defined by the extent $c(\theta - \tau)$, the greatest value of the integral is $f[c(\theta - \tau, \theta - \tau]$. Thus

$$f(c_f,\theta) = \text{Max} \left[ \int_{\theta-\tau}^\theta r(c,T) \, dt + f[c(\theta - \tau), \theta - \tau] \right]. \qquad (2)$$

But if $\tau$ is small

$$f[c(\theta - \tau), \theta - \tau] = f[c(\theta), \theta] + [c(\theta - \tau) - c_f] \frac{\partial f}{\partial c_f} - \tau \frac{\partial f}{\partial \theta} + 0(\tau^2)$$

and

$$c(\theta - \tau) - c_f = \tau r(c_f, T_f) + 0(\tau^2).$$

Putting this together with the abbreviations $f_c = \partial f/\partial c_f$, $f_\theta = \partial f/\partial \theta$ and letting $\tau \to 0$ we have

$$f_\theta = \text{Max} \, r(c_f, T_f)\{1 + f_c\}. \qquad (3)$$

Here the maximization is by correct choice of $T_f$, subject to the restriction (7.1.5), and hence

$$f_\theta = R(c_f)\{1 + f_c\}. \qquad (4)$$

The solution of this equation is rather simple but we will take the occasion to introduce the method of characteristics which is of wide application later. The boundary condition on (4) is that $f \equiv 0$ when $\theta = 0$. Consequently for any value of $c_f$, say $c_e$, we have the values

$$c_f = c_e, \quad \theta = f = f_c = 0, \quad f_\theta = R(c_e), \quad T_f = T_m(c_e) \qquad (5)$$

where $T_m(u)$ is the value of $T$ that maximizes $r(u,T)$. The characteristic equations of (4) are

140

$$\frac{dc_f}{ds} = -R(c_f), \quad \frac{d\theta}{ds} = 1, \quad \frac{df}{ds} = R(c_f)$$

$$\frac{df_c}{ds} = R'(c_f)\{1 + f_c\}, \quad \frac{df_\theta}{ds} = 0. \tag{6}$$

In this simple problem not all these equations are needed. Dividing the first by the second gives $dc_f/d\theta = -R(c_f)$ which is simply the defining Eq. (7.1.1) with the optimal policy $T = T_m$ in use. This is important for it shows that the characteristics of the partial differential equation (3) are actual trajectories or reaction paths. The principle of optimality thus shows that the optimal temperature policy for any reaction is just the temperature specified in the integration of (6) along the characteristic. Separating variables we have

$$\theta = \int_{c_f}^{c_e} \frac{dc}{R(c)} \tag{7}$$

which is identical with (1.9) and shows that the problem of finding the minimum holding time for a given conversion is equivalent to that of finding the maximum conversion for a given holding time.

The last of Eqs. (6) has an important meaning, for it implies that $f_\theta$ does not change along a characteristic. We are clearly only interested in trajectories for which $f_\theta > 0$, for if increasing reaction time decreases the yield, the process should have been stopped. Now the regions of the initial space $\theta = 0$ for which $f_\theta > 0$ can be easily determined, and we have the assurance that characteristics emanating from these regions will completely define the whole of the interesting part of the solution. In the simple case considered here $f_\theta = R(c_e)$ will be positive until $c_e$ reaches the equilibrium value of $c$ for temperature $T_*$.

Whenever $T_f$ is strictly between the bounds $T_*, T^*$ it is a solution of the equation

$$r_T(c_f, T_f) = \frac{\partial}{\partial T_f} r(c_f, T_f) = 0. \tag{8}$$

In this case we might solve (8) simultaneously with

$$f_\theta = r(c_f, T_f)\{1 + f_c\}. \tag{9}$$

The characteristic equations for this are

141

$$\frac{dc_f}{ds} = -r(c_f, T_f)$$

$$\frac{d\theta}{ds} = 1 \tag{10}$$

$$\frac{df}{ds} = r(c_f, T_f)$$

and we can derive an equation for $T_f$ by differentiating (8) along the characteristic, namely:

$$\frac{dT_f}{ds} = \frac{r_{Tc}}{r_{TT}} r(c_f, T_f). \tag{11}$$

Now the first equation of (10) and Eq. (11) can be solved simultaneously and the optimal policy generated as the reaction proceeds. These free equations can only come into play when $T_f$ increases above $T_*$, and when $T_f$ has reached the value $T^*$ it must be held there and Eq. (10) integrated alone. Trite though these observations may seem in this simple case, they are in fact the methods that will be generalized for use in more difficult problems.

Two other problems are solved by the preceding analysis. The first is the Lagrange multiplier formulation of the problem in which the maximum of $c_e - c_f - \lambda\theta$ would be sought. Here the process should cease as soon as the value of the reaction rate at the exit drops to $\lambda$; that is, $c_e$ is given by

$$R(c_e) = \lambda. \tag{12}$$

Thus

$$f_\lambda(c_f) = \text{Max}\,(c_e - c_f - \lambda\theta) = \int_{c_f}^{c_e} \left\{1 - \frac{\lambda}{R(c)}\right\} dc \tag{13}$$

where $c_e$ is given by (12). The second problem implicitly solved is the one with a general material objective function $v(c_1, \ldots c_n)$. If the function $v(c) = v(c_{10} + \alpha_1 c, \ldots c_{n0} + \alpha_n c)$ is monotonic we would seek to maximize $c$, whereas if it has a maximum for some $c = c_e$ we would require to react to just this extent.

## 7.3. Two Consecutive Reactions

In this section we will take up the system of reactions $A \rightarrow B \rightarrow C$, which has been used by Amundson and Bilous (1956) to illustrate the general case. It will be valuable to arrive at their equations from the dynamic programming approach and to clear up two points that they left to be resolved. Let us follow them in assuming that B is the valuable product whose yield is to be maximized and that the kinetics of the reaction lead to the equations

$$\frac{dx}{dt} = a(T)F(x) \tag{1}$$

$$\frac{dy}{dt} = -na(T)F(x) + b(T)G(y). \tag{2}$$

Here $x$ and $y$ are the concentrations of A and B respectively, $a(T)$ and $b(T)$ are rate constants of the usual Arrhenius form, and $t$ is the holding time from the end of the reactor. The functions $F$ and $G$ and the constant $n$ allow of a variety of reactions of this type to be assimilated to a common form (Amundson and Bilous, 1956, p. 88).

The objective function is the yield of B,

$$y(0) - y(\theta) = \int_0^\theta \{na(T)F(x) - b(T)G(y)\}\, dt \tag{3}$$

which has to be maximized by choice of $T(t)$, $0 \le t \le \theta$. When this has been achieved the resulting maximum will be a function only of $x(\theta)$, $y(\theta)$, $\theta$. Let us denote $x(\theta)$ and $y(\theta)$ by $\xi$ and $\eta$ respectively and write

$$f(\xi,\eta,\theta) = \text{Max} \int_0^\theta (naF - bG)\, dt. \tag{4}$$

Then making the usual division of the integral into two integrals over $(\theta, \theta - \tau)$ and $(\theta - \tau, 0)$, and using the principle of optimality on the latter,

$$f(\xi,\eta,\theta) = \text{Max}\left[\int_{\theta-\tau}^\theta (naF - bG)\, dt + f\{x(\theta - \tau), y(\theta - \tau), \theta - \tau)\}\right]. \tag{5}$$

Letting $\tau \to 0$ we are led as usual to a partial differential equation

$$f_\theta = \text{Max}\left[\{na(T)F(\xi) - b(T)G(\eta)\}(1 + f_\eta) - a(T)F(\xi)f_\xi\right] \tag{6}$$

where the maximization is by correct choice of $T = T(\theta)$ subject to the usual restriction

$$T_* \le T \le T^*. \tag{7}$$

The method of characteristics can be usefully employed on Eq. (6)

143

for it is subject to the boundary condition $f = 0$ on the plane $\theta = 0$. Since $a$ and $b$ are both functions of $T$, one is a function of the other and it is an advantage to think of $b$ as a function of $a$ and let $a$ be treated as the policy variable. Denote $db/da = (db/dT)/(da/dT)$ by $A(a)$ and the bounds on $a$ by $a_*, a^*$, where $a_* = a(T_*)$ and $a^* = a(T^*)$. Then if $a$ lies in the interval $(a_*, a^*)$ it is the solution of

$$0 = \{nF(\xi) - A(a)G(\eta)\}(1 + f_\eta) - F(\xi)f_\xi, \qquad (8)$$

and to get a normal form of partial differential equation we should eliminate $a$ between Eq. (8) and

$$f_\theta = \{naF(\xi) - b(a)G(\eta)\}(1 + f_\eta) - aF(\xi)f_\xi. \qquad (9)$$

We shall discuss a case later where this is explicitly possible, but it is not always to be expected that this will come about. Even though the direct elimination is impractical we can proceed by the methods of Section 2.5 and obtain the following characteristic equations:

$$\frac{d\xi}{ds} = aF(\xi)$$

$$\frac{d\eta}{ds} = -naF(\xi) + b(a)G(\eta)$$

$$\frac{d\theta}{ds} = 1$$

$$\frac{df_\xi}{ds} = -aF'(\xi)f_\xi + naF'(\xi)(1 + f_\eta) \qquad (10)$$

$$\frac{df_\eta}{ds} = -b(a)G'(\eta)(1 + f_\eta)$$

$$\frac{df_\theta}{ds} = 0.$$

If now we differentiate the relation (8) along a characteristic and use Eqs. (10) we have

$$\frac{da}{ds} = -nB(a)\frac{F(\xi)G'(\eta)}{G(\eta)} \qquad (11)$$

where

$$B(a) = \{b(a) - aA(a)\}/A'(a). \qquad (12)$$

Equation (11) is remarkable for its simplicity, for we had no reason to suppose that $f_\xi$ and $f_\eta$ would disappear. It will be shown later

144

that this simplicity obtains only for two simultaneous reactions. For kinetic constants $a$ and $b$ of the form $k^* \exp\{-E/RT\}$ the function $B$ is always negative so that $da/ds$ is positive. This would lead us to suppose that the optimal temperature policy is always to decrease the temperature as the reaction proceeds, but this conclusion depends on the applicability of Eq. (8) and we shall see later that care is needed in interpreting this.

The first two equations of (10) and Eq. (11) are identical (apart from the sign of $s$) with Eqs. (25), (26), and (32) of Amundson and Bilous (1956), and it is interesting to have derived them by such entirely different methods. We solve our equations by integrating back from the exit conditions, so that if inlet conditions and the total holding time are given, some trial and error will be needed before the required reaction path is found. In the form in which Amundson and Bilous derived their equations they integrated them in the direction of flow of the reactants and so knew the inlet composition. They had no means however of determining the optimal inlet temperature if the total holding time were given, and so made a choice of inlet temperature and determined the length of process for which it was optimal by the vanishing of a so-called zero function $(nF - AG)$. We notice that this is just our condition (8) on the initial plane $\theta = 0$, for $f = f_\eta = 0$ there. More recently Katz (1960a,b) has applied the method of Weierstrass to these problems. He arrives at a similar set of equations but with two-point boundary conditions and so is again forced into a certain amount of trial and error. It would seem that this is a consequence of the fact that the policy is no longer disjoint. The chief advantage of dynamic programming is that it accommodates the restriction (7) more naturally than the other methods. Such a restriction is essential, for an infinite temperature is required if $G(\eta) = 0$ and this would be the case with a feed of pure A.

We may now turn to the example of first-order reactions to show some concrete results. In this case $n = 1$, $F(\xi) = \xi$ and $G(\eta) = \eta$ and we will put $a(T) = k_1^* \exp(-E_1/RT)$, $b(T) = k_2^* \exp(-E_2/RT)$. Then

$$b(a) = \rho a^{1/r}, \quad r = E_1/E_2, \quad \rho = k_2^* k_1^{*-1/r}. \tag{13}$$

On the initial plane $\theta = 0$ the optimal value of $a$ is the one that makes $(a\xi - b\eta)$ greatest. Now the derivative of $(a\xi - b\eta)$ vanishes when

$$a^{(1-r)/r} = \frac{r\xi}{\rho\eta} \tag{14}$$

and the second derivative of $(a\xi - b\eta)$ at this point is $(r-1)b\eta/r^2a^2$, so that only when $r < 1(E_2 > E_1)$ does this give a maximum. If $r > 1$, the stationary point is a relative minimum and the maximum reaction rate is to be found when $T = T^*$ if this makes $(a\xi - b\eta)$ positive. Since we know that $a$ must not decrease along a characteristic and it is already at its maximum, the optimal policy is to hold $T$ at $T^*$. This rather insipid policy corresponds to the case of a single endothermic reaction and confirms Amundson's doubt as to the applicability of his methods to this case.

If $r < 1$, there are three regions of importance in the initial plane. Let $R = r/(1-r)$; then these regions are

I: $(1/\rho)a_*^{-1/R} \geq \eta/\xi \geq (r/\rho)a_*^{-1/R}$      where $a = a_*$

II: $(r/\rho)a_*^{-1/R} \geq \eta/\xi \geq (r/\rho)a^{*-1/R}$      where $a^* \geq a \geq a_*$

III: $(r/\rho)a^{*-1/R} \geq \eta/\xi \geq 0$      where $a = a^*$.

A characteristic emanating from the last of these must have $a = a^*$ all the way along it and so is obtained by integrating the first two of Eqs. (10) until either $\xi$ or $\eta$ becomes negative. If the characteristic emanates from region (II) the initial value of $a$ is given by (14) and Eqs. (10) and (11) are integrated until the value of $a$ reaches $a^*$, after which $a$ is held constant. From region (III) the initial value of $a$ is $a_*$ and it is held to this until the solution of (8), namely

$$(r\xi - \rho a^{1/R}\eta)(1 + f_\eta) - r\xi f_\xi = 0,$$

reaches $a_*$. From this point on the integration is as in (II). In this way the whole of the interesting part of $\xi, \eta, \theta$ space is traversed by trajectories, and surfaces of constant policy can be drawn.

It is difficult however to visualize clearly this three-dimensional situation and we therefore make use of the homogeneity belonging to the order of the reactions to reduce the number of dimensions. Let $z = y/x$; then from Eqs. (1) and (2) we have

$$\frac{dz}{dt} = -a + (b-a)z. \tag{15}$$

Also, the maximum yield of B will be proportional to the inlet concentration of A, $x(\theta) = \xi$. Therefore let

$$f(\xi,\eta,\theta) = \xi g(\zeta,\theta) \tag{16}$$

where

$$\zeta = \eta/\xi. \tag{17}$$

Since $f_\theta = \xi g_\theta$, $f_\xi = g - \zeta g_\zeta$, $f_\eta = g_\zeta$, we have in place of Eq. (6)

$$g_\theta = \text{Max}\left[(a - b\zeta)(1 + g_\zeta) - a(g - \zeta g_\zeta)\right] \tag{18}$$

Now since $b = \rho a^{1/r}$ it is possible to find the maximizing value of $a$ explicitly and eliminate it from Eq. (18). We have

$$a = \left[\frac{r}{\rho}\frac{1 + (1 + \zeta)g_\zeta - g}{\zeta(1 + g_\zeta)}\right]^{1/R} \tag{19}$$

and

$$g_\theta = (1 - r)\left(\frac{r}{\rho}\right)^R \frac{\{1 + (1 + \zeta)g_\zeta - g\}^{R+1}}{\zeta^R(1 + g_\zeta)^R}. \tag{20}$$

This is now a perfectly normal, though highly nonlinear, first order partial differential equation, of which we can write down the characteristic equations. They are

$$\frac{d\zeta}{ds} = -a + (b - a)\zeta \tag{21}$$

$$\frac{d\theta}{ds} = 1 \tag{22}$$

$$\frac{dg}{ds} = a(1 - g) - b\zeta g_\zeta \tag{23}$$

$$\frac{dg_\zeta}{ds} = b(1 + g_\zeta) \tag{24}$$

$$\frac{dg_\theta}{ds} = ag_\theta \tag{25}$$

whence

$$\frac{da}{ds} = -\frac{ra^2}{\zeta} \tag{26}$$

Formidable though these may seem it is actually possible to find a solution in finite terms. Dividing (21) by (26) we have a Riccati equation for $\zeta$ as a function of $a$. If $\beta(a)$ denotes $(b - a)/ra^2$, then

$$\zeta = \zeta_0 \frac{\exp\{\beta(a)\}/a^{1/R}\beta(a)}{\exp\{\beta(a_0)\}/a_0^{1/r}\beta(a_0) + \zeta_0 \int_{a_0}^{a} a^{-1/r}\exp\{\beta(a)\}\,da} \tag{27}$$

is the solution for which $\zeta = \zeta_0$ when $a = a_0$. However, this solution would be difficult to compute, for the next step is to substitute (27)

147

back into (26) and determine $s$ as a function of $a$. It is more congenial to the digital computer to solve these equations as they stand.

The equations (21)$_-$(26) apply when $a$ is in the interval $(a_*, a^*)$; when $a$ is held constant they can be immediately integrated to give

$$g(\zeta, \theta) = \frac{e^{-a\theta} - e^{-b\theta}}{(b/a) - 1} - \zeta(1 - e^{-b\theta}), \tag{28}$$

$a$ and $b$ being evaluated at the constant temperature $T_*$ or $T^*$. The general form of this solution for the interesting region $g_\theta > 0$ is shown in Fig. 7.5. This solution allows us to dismiss the case $r = 1$ for which temperature has no effect on the relative rates of the two reactions. It follows that where the concentrations of A and B favor the formation of B the reaction should proceed as rapidly as possible, i.e., $T = T^*$, and the fixed-temperature solution (28) applies. When the concentrations cease to favor the formation of B the reaction should cease. Likewise, we have seen that $T = T^*$ is the optimal policy in case $r > 1$ so that the solution (28) applies also here. Figure 7.6 shows a typical solution for $r > 1$.

A solution for $r < 1$ is shown by Figs. 7.7 through 7.10. $\zeta_*$ and $\zeta^*$ denote the values of $(r/\rho)a^{-1/R}$ at $a = a^*$ and $a = a_*$ respectively, so that the three regions described above and corresponding initial values of $a$ and $g_\theta$ are

I: $\zeta^*/r \geq \zeta \geq \zeta^*$: $a = a_*$: $g_\theta = a_* - b_*\zeta$
II: $\zeta^* \geq \zeta \geq \zeta_*$: $a_* \leq a \leq a^*$: $g_\theta = (1 - r)(r/\rho\zeta)^R$
III: $\zeta_* \geq \zeta \geq 0$: $a = a^*$: $g_\theta = a^* - b^*\zeta$.

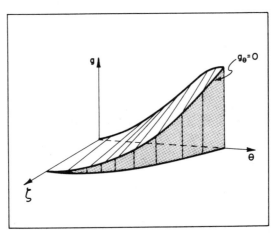

FIG. 7.5. The yield surface for constant temperature.

148

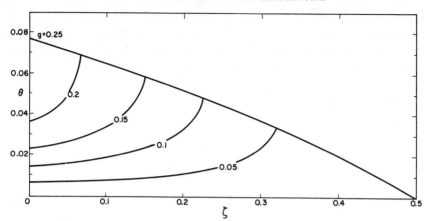

FIG. 7.6. The optimal yield for $r > 1$ ($r = 2$, $\rho = 6$, $a^* = 9$).

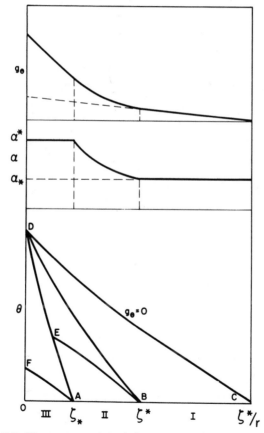

FIG. 7.7. The construction of the optimal yield surface ($r < 1$).

149

## 7. THE TUBULAR REACTOR

The upper parts of Fig. 7.7 show this initial policy for $a$ and corresponding $g_\theta$: it can be shown that $g_\theta$ has a continuous derivative and this amply assures the existence of the solution of the partial differential equation (20). Any characteristic emanating from the region (I) starts with $a = a_*$ and maintains this value until the right-hand side of (19) reaches $a_*$. Since it is a region of constant temperature the solution (28) applies and we can determine the arc BD across which $a$ increases above $a_*$ analytically; it is

$$\zeta = \zeta^* \frac{(b_*/a_*) - \exp(b_* - a_*)\theta}{(b_*/a_*) - 1} = \zeta^* B(\theta). \qquad (29)$$

It meets the axis $\zeta = 0$ at the same point as the curve $g_\theta = 0$ whose equation is $\zeta = \zeta^* B(\theta)/r$. Beyond the line BD the full characteristic equations apply until $a$ reaches $a^*$ on ED, after which it is held constant. Characteristics emanating from region (II) (AB) have $a$ in the range $(a_*, a^*)$ until they meet the arc AE after which $a = a^*$. Characteristics starting on OA all lie below AF, and $a = a^*$ on all.

The results of such an integration are shown in Fig. 7.8 for $r = 0.5$, $\rho = 5$, $a_* = 0.1$, and $a^* = 0.4$. The broken lines are characteristics

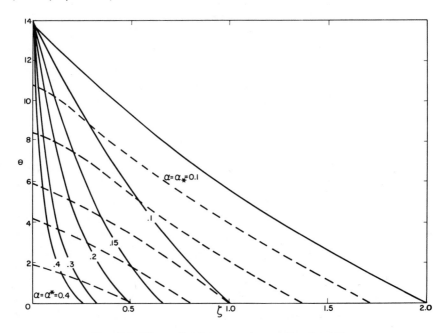

FIG. 7.8. The optimal temperature policy $(r < 1)$.

while the full ones are of constant-temperature policy. The resulting optimal yield surface is shown in Fig. 7.9.

The difference between a disjoint policy and one that is not is clearly seen by comparing Figs. 7.4 and 7.10. With a disjoint policy a given feed condition requires the same inlet temperature whatever the total holding time of the process. Variation of holding time merely takes one farther along the profile. With a policy which is not disjoint, however, the same feed condition will demand different

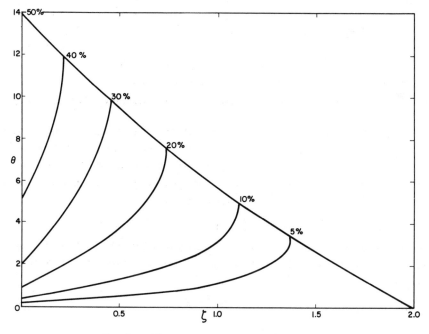

FIG. 7.9. The optimal yield surface ($r < 1$).

policies for different lengths. For instance with a feed of pure A the greatest attainable yield of B is 50 per cent. This occurs with a reactor of holding time $\theta = 13.8$ and the minimum permitted temperature $a = a_*$; the corresponding characteristic is the boundary $g_\theta = 0$ of Fig. 7.8. If the reactor has a holding time of only 12 the optimal policy is to have a very short section at maximum temperature followed by a steeply falling profile and a long final section at minimum temperature; the yield is then 48 per cent. As the total holding time gets smaller the yield falls, the high-temperature inlet section gets longer and the falling profile less steep.

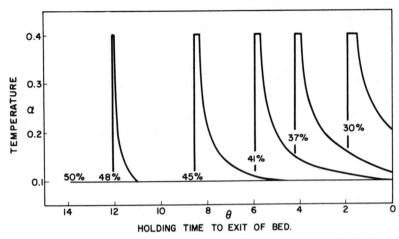

FIG. 7.10. Temperature profiles for various lengths of reactor and feed of pure A.

This incidentally resolves a paradox that Amundson suggested, namely, that an infinitely long reactor at zero temperature should give the complete conversion of A to B. This is indeed the case, for Fig. 7.9 shows that for any feed composition $\zeta$ the best yield is given by a reactor of length satisfying

$$r\zeta = \zeta^* B(\theta)$$

[see Eq. (29)] using the constant-temperature policy $T = T_*$. As $T_*$ decreases this value of $\theta$ increases without bound. For $\zeta = 0$ we have

$$\theta = \frac{\ln (b_*/a_*)}{b_* - a_*} \qquad (30)$$

and a maximum yield of

$$g = (b_*/a_*)^{b_*/(a_*-b_*)}. \qquad (31)$$

Analogous formulas could be written down for any $\zeta$ but they are unpleasantly ugly.

## 7.4. *Two Simultaneous Reactions in General*

Before giving a completely general treatment of any number of simultaneous reactions, we will remark that for two reactions certain of the simplifying features of the last section are retained. If $c^1$ and $c^2$ denote the extents of the two reactions, then according to

152

Chapter 3 we can write the equations for the tubular reactor in the form

$$\frac{dc^1}{dt} = -r^1(c^1,c^2,T),\tag{1}$$

$$\frac{dc^2}{dt} = -r^2(c^1,c^2,T),\tag{2}$$

$$c_i = c_{i0} + \alpha_{i1}c^1 + \alpha_{i2}c^2, \qquad i = 1, \ldots n.\tag{3}$$

Let

$$v(c_1, \ldots c_n) = v(c^1,c^2;c_{10}, \ldots c_{n0}) = v(c^1,c^2)$$

be the value of unit volume of the mixture when the concentration of $A_i$ is $c_i$; then the general material objective function we wish to consider is

$$v[c^1(0),c^2(0)] - v[c^1(\theta),c^2(\theta)].\tag{4}$$

If $v$ is continuous and piecewise differentiable we may write this as

$$\int_0^\theta \left( \frac{\partial v}{\partial c^1} r^1 + \frac{\partial v}{\partial c^2} r^2 \right) dt.$$

We now see that when the optimal policy has been chosen the resulting maximum will be a function of $c^1(\theta)$, $c^2(\theta)$ and $\theta$, and we write

$$f(u_1,u_2,\theta) = \text{Max} \left[ \int_0^\theta (v_1 r^1 + v_2 r^2) \, dt \right]\tag{5}$$

where $u_1$ and $u_2$ denote $c^1(\theta)$ and $c^2(\theta)$ respectively and $v_i$ denotes $\partial v/\partial c^i$. The process of splitting this integral into two parts, using the principle of optimality on the one and letting the other tend to zero, which should now be familiar to the reader, leads immediately to the partial differential equation

$$f_\theta = \text{Max} \left[ (v_1 + f_1)r^1(u_1,u_2,w) + (v_2 + f_2)r^2(u_1,u_2,w) \right]\tag{6}$$

where $f_i$ denotes $\partial f/\partial u_i$ and $w = T(\theta)$. This equation is to be solved subject to the condition $f \equiv 0$ on $\theta = 0$; i.e., at any point $u_1$, $u_2$, $\theta = 0$, $f = f_1 = f_2 = 0$, $f_\theta = \text{Max} (v_1 r^1 + v_2 r^2)$, and $w$ has the value that yields this maximum.

Now $w = T(\theta)$ is bounded by the usual upper and lower bounds $(T_*,T^*)$, but where the maximum occurs within this interval it satisfies

$$0 = (v_1 + f_1)r_w^1 + (v_2 + f_2)r_w^2,\tag{7}$$

$(r_w$ denotes $\partial r/\partial w)$. Proceeding as usual to the characteristic equations,

$$\frac{du_i}{ds} = -r^i \qquad i = 1,2 \tag{8}$$

$$\frac{d\theta}{ds} = 1 \tag{9}$$

$$\frac{df}{ds} = v_1 r^1 + v_2 r^2 \tag{10}$$

$$\frac{df_i}{ds} = \sum_{j=1}^{2} \{v_{ij}r^j + (v_j + f_j)r_i^j\} \tag{11}$$

$$\frac{df_\theta}{ds} = 0. \tag{12}$$

(Here the suffixes denote differentiation with respect to the appropriate $u$). Differentiating (7) characteristically yields

$$\frac{dw}{ds} = \frac{\displaystyle\sum_{i=1}^{2}\sum_{j=1}^{2} (f_j + v_j)(r_w^i r_i^j - r^i r_{wi}^j)}{\displaystyle\sum_{j=1}^{2} (f_j + v_j)r_{ww}^j}. \tag{13}$$

But this is homogeneous in $(f_1 + v_1)$ and $(f_2 + v_2)$ so that their ratio can be eliminated between (13) and (7) giving

$$\frac{dw}{ds} = \frac{\displaystyle\sum_{i=1}^{2} \{r_w^2(r_w^i r_i^1 - r^i r_{wi}^1) - r_w^1(r_w^i r_i^2 - r^i r_{wi}^2)\}}{(r_w^2 r_{ww}^1 - r_w^1 r_{ww}^2)}. \tag{14}$$

This equation contains only the variables $u_1, u_2$, and $w$ and so can be solved together with the two equations (8). This simplification to an equation for the temperature policy is possible only for two reactions; with more than two the elimination of the partial derivatives of $f$ is no longer possible. Equation (14) is essentially the same as Eq. (28) of Horn's paper (1960).

Equations (8) and (14) give the solution of the problem if $w$, that is, the temperature, is not restricted and if

$$\sum_{i=1}^{2} (v_i + f_i)r_{ww}^i < 0,$$

i.e., Eq. (7) gives a maximum. Even though restrictions are essential, Eq. (14) may be of interest, perhaps indicating, as in the last sec-

154

tion, that the policy is monotonic. The monotonicity of the policy in the interval $T_*,T^*$ implies that the restricted policy consists of at most three sections, one at each of the bounding temperatures and a monotonic section between them.

Under any conditions Eq. (6) can be solved by simultaneously integrating the four equations (8) and (10) and choosing $w$ at each step to be the value that maximizes the right-hand side of (6). If little is known about the structure of the policy a direct numerical search for this value of $w$ is always safe, and is no great problem for the digital computer.

## 7.5. *The General Problem*

Up to this point we have considered an objective function which has been the difference between the concentration or value of the product and that of the feed. It will be convenient in this section to take an objective function which represents the value of the product only. Later this may be built into a more realistic expression for the profit by subtracting the value of the feed, multiplying by the flow rate and subtracting the cost of the operation.

By way of variation (and later to show more easily the connection with other work) let us work with Eqs. (3.4.1) for the mass concentrations. If there are $m$ simultaneous reactions, the first $m$ concentrations $g_1, \ldots g_m$ may be used and the remainder expressed in terms of them by (3.1.12):

$$g_k = g_{k0} + \sum_{i,j=1}^{m} \alpha_{kj}\beta_{ji}(g_i - g_{i0}), \qquad k = m + 1, \ldots n. \qquad (1)$$

Let these be substituted in the reaction rate expression $r^j$, then we have $m$ functions

$$f_i = f_i(g_1, \ldots g_m, T, p) = \sum_{j=1}^{m} \alpha_{ij} r^j \qquad (2)$$

for the rate of formation of $A_i$ in terms of these concentrations the temperature and pressure. Then writing $\theta - t$ for $x/G$ in Eqs. (3.4.1) we have

$$dg_i/dt = -f_i(g_1, \ldots g_m, T, p), \qquad i = 1, \ldots m. \qquad (3)$$

We will suppose $T$ and $p$ both controllable, as they would be in a

155

batch reactor; in the tubular reactor this might not be the case. The temperature and pressure are bounded in the usual way,

$$T_* \leq T \leq T^* \tag{4}$$

$$p_* \leq p \leq p^*. \tag{5}$$

The objective function will be

$$V[g_1(0), \ldots g_m(0)] \tag{6}$$

and is assumed to be piecewise continuous and differentiable. This is general enough to include specifications of the type that set $V = 0$ outside a certain region.

We now recognize that from any point on a given optimal path we arrive at the same value of the objective function. Let

$$\phi(u_1, \ldots u_m, \theta) = \text{Max } V[g_1(0), \ldots g_m(0)], \tag{7}$$

where $u_i = g_i(\theta)$ is the feed state and $\theta$ the total holding time. Then by the principle of optimality

$$\phi(u_1, \ldots u_m, \theta) = \text{Max } \phi[g_1(\theta - \tau), \ldots g_m(\theta - \tau), \theta - \tau] \tag{8}$$

for any $\tau$, $0 \leq \tau \leq \theta$; the maximization is attained by choice of the policy $T(t), p(t)$ on the interval $\theta - \tau \leq t \leq \theta$ and $g_i(\theta - \tau)$ is the result of this policy obtained by integrating Eqs. (3). Letting $\tau \to 0$ we have, with the usual notation,

$$\phi_\theta = \text{Max} \sum_{i=1}^{m} \phi_i f_i. \tag{9}$$

This equation has to be solved subject to the boundary condition

$$\phi(u_1, \ldots u_m, 0) = V(u_1, \ldots u_m). \tag{10}$$

The characteristic equations are

$$\frac{du_i}{ds} = -f_i, \qquad i = 1, \ldots m, \tag{11}$$

$$\frac{d\theta}{ds} = 1 \tag{12}$$

$$\frac{d\phi}{ds} = 0 \tag{13}$$

$$\frac{d\phi_i}{ds} = \sum_{j=1}^{m} \phi_j f_{j,i}, \qquad i = 1, \ldots m, \tag{14}$$

$$\frac{d\phi_\theta}{ds} = 0 \tag{15}$$

where $f_{j,i}$ denotes $\partial f_j/\partial u_i$. For any point $(u_1, \ldots u_m)$ of the boundary for which $V$ is differentiable we have the initial values for Eqs. (12)–(15)

$$\theta = 0, \quad \phi = V, \quad \phi_i = \partial V/\partial u_i$$

$$\phi_\theta = \text{Max} \sum_{i=1}^{m} f_i(\partial V/\partial u_i) \tag{16}$$

and values of $T$ and $p$ that make this last term maximum. The integration of the characteristic differential equations proceeds from these initial values; at each step $T$ and $p$ are chosen so that the expression on the right side of (9) is maximum. The only equations that really enter into this process are the $2m$ equations (11) and (14), for (12), (13) and (15) are trivial. The initial condition on $\phi_\theta$ serves to define the area $\phi_\theta > 0$ from which characteristics will be profitable reaction paths. It also distinguishes within this area nine subregions according to the inequalities (4) and (5). These may be indicated schematically for the two variables $T$ and $p$ as in Table 7.1.

TABLE 7.1

| $T = T_*$ <br> $p = p^*$ | $T_* \leq T \leq T^*$ <br> $p = p^*$ | $T = T^*$ <br> $p = p^*$ |
|---|---|---|
| $T = T_*$ <br> $p_* \leq p \leq p^*$ | $T_* \leq T \leq T^*$ <br> $p_* \leq p \leq p^*$ | $T = T^*$ <br> $p_* \leq p \leq p^*$ |
| $T = T_*$ <br> $p = p_*$ | $T_* \leq T \leq T^*$ <br> $p = p_*$ | $T = T^*$ <br> $p = p_*$ |

They are regions of initial plane and a characteristic may pass from one condition to another during integration. It is clear that even with the two variables $p$ and $T$ the process of finding the maximum of (9) is not too easy even when the function is unimodal. Under certain circumstances the method mentioned above in Section 2.4 can be used, for there is often a simplifying monotonicity in physical situations. However, it is not to be trusted without considerable insight into the physical system.

The identity of the characteristic equations with those derived by Katz (1960a) by methods of the calculus of variations is now clear. In his notation $\phi_i = v_i$, $s = -t$, and his basic problem is that of maximizing the yield of $A_2$. This is equivalent to setting $V(u_i, \ldots u_m) = u_2$, whence the initial values of $\phi_i = v_i$ are 1 if $i = 2$

or zero otherwise. Our equations (11), (14) and (16) are identical with his equation (6) in the reference cited, and his maximizing condition (7) is equivalent to our equation (9). Other modifications of the basic problem are considered and it will be found that they correspond to appropriate changes in $V$. In another paper Katz (1960b) has addressed the specific problem of temperature and pressure control and arrived at equations identical with those presented here. The identity of our equations with those of Horn (1960) is also easy to see. Horn's functions $v_i$ are here called $-f_i$ and his quantities $\lambda_i$ are our $\phi_i$. Consequently his equations (37a) and (38a) correspond exactly to Eqs. (14) and (16) here. In favor of the dynamic programming approach it may be said that the physical meaning of the $\phi_i$ is much easier to apprehend than that of the $v_i$ or $\lambda_i$ introduced in the methods of the calculus of variations.

When product specifications are included such as the requirement that

$$g_{i*} \leq g_i(0) = u_i \leq g_i^*$$ (17)

our problem is even simpler, for now only characteristics emanating from this part of the initial plane are relevant.

# 8

# Stochastic Problems

*"Introduce me, now there's a good fellow," he said,*
*"If we happen to meet it together!"*
*And the Bellman, sagaciously nodding his head,*
*Said "That must depend on the weather."*

In this chapter we will review three stochastic problems that have been considered. Much remains to be done in this area and it will be of increasing importance in opening up the way to adaptive control problems. The feature common to such problems is that to some extent they "depend on the weather," the outcome of a certain stage not being known precisely but only in a probabilistic sense. In some cases (for example, the second one discussed here) it is possible to arrive at equations that are deterministic but whose solution is interpreted in stochastic terms when going back to the physical problem.

The first example is due to Rudd (1960) and concerns the optimal number of replications of the preparation of chemicals needed in a main process. If these preparations are subject to failure and if it is quite essential that they should be available without delay to the main process, it will be advisable to prepare more than one batch but this will become expensive if too many are prepared. The second example is a transliteration into manufacturing terms of Bellman's stochastic gold mining process (1957, Chapter 2). The third is a consideration of some of the simpler models of catalyst replacement policy that have been discussed by Roberts (1960a,b).

## 8.1. *Optimal Replication of Processes Subject to Failure*

The process we wish to consider is one in which a primary chemical species is modified by reaction with a number of secondary species $A_N, \ldots A_1$ in succession. These secondary species have to be prepared specially for the appropriate stage of the process and must be available at the right time; otherwise the whole process is rendered valueless. Such unstable preparations are not uncommon in biochemical engineering. If the preparation of $A_n$, $n = 1, \ldots N$, is subject to random failure, the preparation of more than one batch of it will increase the probability of its being available at the right time. However, this must be carefully balanced against the increased cost of these extra preparations and a problem of optimal specification arises. The system is illustrated in Fig. 8.1; $r_n$ denotes the number of batches of $A_n$ that are prepared.

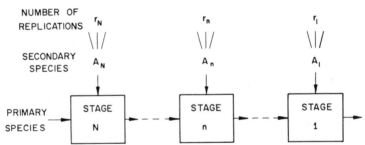

NUMBER OF REPLICATIONS  $r_N$  $r_n$  $r_1$

SECONDARY SPECIES  $A_N$  $A_n$  $A_1$

PRIMARY SPECIES

STAGE N   STAGE n   STAGE 1

FIG. 8.1. Production process considered in Section 8.1.

Let $p_n$ be the probability of failure of any batch in the preparation of $A_n$. It is assumed that the failure of any batch is independent of the others, so that the probability of all $r_n$ batches failing is $p_n^{r_n}$. It follows that the probability of at least one batch succeeding is $1 - p_n^{r_n} = q_n$, say. Let $c_n(r_n)$ be the cost of preparing $r_n$ batches of $A_n$, a function that need not be linear, $v$ the value of the final product, and $C$ the cost of the primary species. $Q_N$ is the probability that the whole process is successful; we expect to gain $vP_N$ at a cost of $\sum_1^N c_n(r_n) + C$. We may therefore take as objective function

$$P_N = vQ_N - \sum c_n(r_n) - C,$$
$$= v\Pi q_n - \sum c_n(r_n) - C, \qquad (1)$$

since $Q_N = \Pi q_n$. $P_N$ is a function not only of the policy $r_1, \ldots r_N$, which must now be chosen optimally, but also of the probability with which the primary species is available. In the case of the full $N$ stage process this is a certainty but in dynamic programming we consider the product of stage $N$ to be the primary species for the subsequent $N - 1$ stage process. We are thus led to define

$$f_N(b_{N+1}) = \text{Max } P_N, \text{ when } r_1, \ldots r_N \text{ is optimally} \tag{2}$$
chosen and $b_{N+1}$ is the probability that
the primary species is available.

From this definition we can derive a functional equation by the principle of optimality

$$f_N(b_{N+1}) = \text{Max } \{f_{N-1}(b_N) - c_N(r_N)\} \tag{3}$$

where the maximization is to be secured by the right choice of $r_N$. Since $b_N$ is the probability that material is available for the remaining $(N - 1)$ stages it is the product of $b_{N+1}$, the probability of its being available to stage $N$, and $q_N$, the probability of success at stage $N$. Thus

$$b_N = q_N b_{N+1} = (1 - p_N^{r_N})b_{N+1} \tag{4}$$

provides the relation between $b_{N+1}$, $b_N$ and $r_N$ required for the solution of (3). This sequence of equations is started with the single-stage problem

$$f_1(b_2) = \text{Max } \{vq_1 b_2 - c_1(r_1) - C\}. \tag{5}$$

How advantageous this design may be in comparison with a strictly stoichiometric design will be seen from the following example where a probable loss is turned to a probable gain. Let W be the primary species and Z the final product obtained as the result of the following reactions:

$$W + A_3 \rightarrow X$$
$$X + A_2 \rightarrow Y$$
$$Y + A_1 \rightarrow Z.$$

We will suppose that W is of negligible cost but that the cost of preparation of $A_1$, $A_2$ and $A_3$ is 1.0, 1.0 and 0.2 units/batch respectively and that the value of Z is 10 units. Also let $p_1 = 1/4$, $p_2 = 1/2$, $p_3 = 2/3$.

A stoichiometric design calls for only one batch of each secondary species to be prepared at a total cost of 2.2 units. The probability of their being simultaneously successful is

$$\left(1 - \frac{1}{4}\right)\left(1 - \frac{1}{2}\right)\left(1 - \frac{2}{3}\right) = \frac{1}{8}$$

so that the expected gain is 1.25 units. Thus on an average we can expect to make a loss of 0.95 units.

The solution of Eqs. (3), (4), and (5) for these constants is summarized in Table 8.1. Only one line is given in section 3 since we know that W is certainly available and so $b_4 = 1$. From it we see that 7 batches of $A_3$ should be prepared, with a resulting probability of 0.94 of successful outcome and an expected net profit of 1.28 units. Interpolating in the second section for $b_3 = 0.94$, we have $r_2 = 3$ for the optimal number of batches of $A_2$ and $b_2 = 0.83$. From the first section we now find that two batches of $A_1$ should be prepared. Thus a process with probable loss of 0.95 units has been converted to one of a probable gain of 1.28 units, which is quite satisfactory.

TABLE 8.1

| $n$ | $b_{n+1}$ | $f_n(b_{n+1})$ | $r_n$ | $b_n$ |
|---|---|---|---|---|
| 1 | 0.2 | 0.50 | 1 | — |
|   | 0.4 | 2.00 | 1 | — |
|   | 0.6 | 3.63 | 2 | — |
|   | 0.8 | 5.50 | 2 | — |
|   | 1.0 | 7.38 | 2 | — |
| 2 | 0.4 | 0.00 | 0 | 0.00 |
|   | 0.6 | 0.30 | 2 | 0.45 |
|   | 0.8 | 1.63 | 2 | 0.60 |
|   | 0.9 | 2.30 | 3 | 0.79 |
|   | 1.0 | 3.15 | 3 | 0.88 |
| 3 | 1.0 | 1.28 | 7 | 0.94 |

Clearly, the process described is only one of many that might be treated along similar lines. We might include the possibility of failure at any one of the main stages. It might be that X and Y are not unstable so that following the successful outcome of stage $(n + 1)$ it would be possible to start the preparation of $A_n$. If we put a value on the time it takes to prepare, it will again be desirable to prepare more than one batch at a time. Other problems of this kind, some of which are not amenable to dynamic programming, have been discussed by Rudd (1960) and Westbrook (1961).

## 8.2. *Stochastic Gold Making*

Another stochastic process we may consider is a chemical engineering version of Bellman's gold-mining process (Bellman 1957, Chapter 2). We suppose we have two sources of supply of a raw material with slightly different characteristics. Of the material from the source A, of which there is a total quantity $x$, it would be possible to convert a fraction $r$ with probability $p$, but there is a probability $(1 - p)$ that the reactor would be put out of action. For B the corresponding quantities are $y, s, q$, and $(1 - q)$ respectively. We want an operating policy which tells us whether to use material from A or B at any stage of production, and this policy is to maximize the total amount of raw material used before the converter is damaged. Such a situation might arise if the sources of supply were liable to contain a catalyst poison.

We suppose in the first instance that at most $N$ stages will be employed, and set

$$f_N(x,y) = \text{maximum amount of raw material expected to be}$$
$$\text{used before the converter is damaged when quan-} \quad (1)$$
$$\text{tities } x \text{ and } y \text{ are available from sources A and B.}$$

For one stage,

$$f_1(x,y) = \text{Max } (prx, qsy) \quad (2)$$

and the policy will be to use material from A if the first term is greater or material from B if the second term is greater. In a two-stage process we may either use from A first, in which case we expect to use a quantity $rx$ with probability $p$ and have left $(1 - r)x, y$, or we can use first from B and use $sy$ with $x, (1 - s)y$ remaining with probability $q$. In the first case the expected amount is

$$p\{rx + f_1[(1 - r)x,y]\},$$

and in the second it is

$$q\{sy + f_1[x,(1 - s)y]\}.$$

Thus

$$f_2(x,y) = \text{Max } \{rx + f_1[(1 - r)x,y], sy + f_1[x,(1 - s)y]\}. \quad (3)$$

163

Clearly, by the same argument,

$$f_N(x,y) = \text{Max } \{rx + f_{N-1}[(1 - r)x,y], sy + f_{N-1}[x,(1 - s)y]\}. \quad (4)$$

If $N \to \infty$ and the functions $f_N$ converge to a single function $f$, (4) will satisfy

$$f(x,y) = \text{Max } \{rx + f[(1 - r)x,y], sy + f[x,(1 - s)y]\}. \quad (5)$$

Bellman (1957, p. 64) proves that a function satisfying this equation exists and is unique and that the $f_N$ converge toward it. What interests us here is the rather simple structure of the optimum and the policy.

The function $f(x,y)$ is homogeneous of the first degree in $x$ and $y$, that is, $f(kx,ky) = kf(x,y)$. This is clear from the construction of $f$ and also from Eq. (5). In other words, if at the point $(x,y)$ of the $x,y$ plane the decision is to use A first, then this is also the optimal decision at all points of the ray from the origin to $(x,y)$. If we were to map the regions of the plane in which the optimal decision is always A, they would consist of one or more sectors with vertex at the origin, and likewise for B. If $x$ greatly exceeds $y$ we would certainly expect to use material from A, so that a sector adjacent to the $x$ axis is an A region, while one near to the $y$ axis is a B region. We now make the assumption that there are only two regions separated by a line L, as shown in Fig. 8.2, and try to determine the line L and afterwards show that this is in fact the case.

If the use of B above the line L and the use of A below it are

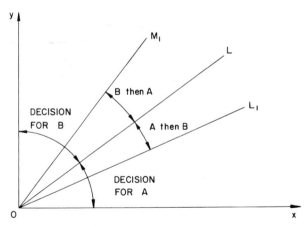

FIG. 8.2. Decision regions in the $x,y$ plane.

optimal, it follows that on the line itself the yield is indifferent to which of the two is used. This leads to the equation

$$prx + pf[(1 - r)x, y] = qsy + q f[x, (1 - s)y],$$

which however is not easy to solve. But another way of saying that it is equally good to use A or B is to say that using A first and then B is equivalent to using B first and then A. Using A first and then B gives

$$prx + pqsy + pq f[(1 - r)x, (1 - s)y],$$

while using B and then A gives

$$qsy + pqrx + pq f[(1 - r)x, (1 - s)y].$$

Identifying these gives

$$\frac{pr}{1 - p} x = \frac{qs}{1 - q} y, \tag{6}$$

which is the equation for L. Above this line the policy BA will be better than the policy AB but on it they are equally good. Equation (6) may be interpreted as saying that the ratio of the probable immediate gain ($prx$ or $qsy$) to the probability of loss ($1 - p$ or $1 - q$) is indifferent to the choice of A or B.

Certainly, on the $x$ axis when there is no B one must use A, so that

$$f(x, 0) = prx + p f[(1 - r)x, 0] > q f(x, 0), \tag{7}$$

and because of the continuity of $f(x, y)$ there must be a sector adjacent to this axis for which

$$f(x, y) > qsy + q f[x, (1 - s)y]$$

and in this region A is the optimal choice. Now consider a point P below L such that $x, (1 - s)y$ is in this region. If B were the optimal first choice at P then the optimal two-stage policy would be BA, but we know that below L the policy AB is better than BA, for $prx/(1 - p)$ exceeds $qsy(1 - q)$. It follows that A must be the optimal choice at P and this argument can be extended all the way up to L. There are thus only two decision regions, and if the state of the supplies is given by $(x, y)$ the optimal decision is to use A or B according as this point lies below or above L.

But the structure of $f(x, y)$ can be explored still further. It is evident that if $(x, y)$ is on the line

$$(1 - r) \frac{pr}{1 - p} x = \frac{qs}{1 - q} y, \tag{8}$$

then the first choice will be to use A, but after this choice the point $[(1 - r)x, y]$ lies on L. Let the line given by (8) be called $L_1$; then in the sector $LOL_1$ the first two choices will be A and then B. Likewise if $M_1$ is the line

$$\frac{pr}{1 - p} x = \frac{qs}{1 - q} y(1 - s)$$

then a point $(x, y)$ on this line is taken into a point on L after the first choice B, and any point in the sector $M_1OL$ requires the first choice B then A. We can generate a sequence of lines $L_n$ and $M_n$, namely:

$$(1 - r)^n \frac{pr}{1 - p} x = \frac{qs}{1 - q} y \quad \text{and} \quad \frac{pr}{1 - p} = \frac{qs}{1 - q} y(1 - s)^n.$$

These are such that in the sector $L_nOL_{n-1}$ the first $n$ decisions for A are followed by one for B, whereas in $M_nOM_{n-1}$, $n$ decisions for B precede one for A. If $r^\alpha = s^\beta$ and $\alpha$ and $\beta$ are integers, it is possible to get an analytical expression for $f$; it is linear within any of the sectors.

It is shown by Bellman that for any $N$ the $x,y$ plane is divided into two decision regions just as in the case of infinite $N$. It is also found that as $N$ increases the decision regions converge monotonically to those for $N = \infty$, and indeed that there is an $N_0$ such that they are identical for $N > N_0$.

## 8.3. *Optimal Catalyst Replacement Policies*

In two papers of great interest, Roberts (1960a,b) has considered the dynamic programming formulation of a catalyst replacement problem. It will not be possible to discuss the whole of his work here as it goes a long way towards a consideration of adaptive control; we shall content ourselves with one of his simpler models which brings out some features of stochastic dynamic programming.

The process he considers is modeled on an endothermic gas-phase catalytic reaction such as is illustrated in Fig. 8.3. A feed of pure A is passed to a reactor in which a fraction $c$ is converted to products X and Y. This stream then goes to a separating unit from which the unconverted A is returned to the feed stream and the products

166

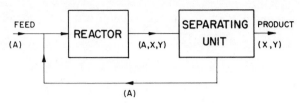

FIG. 8.3. The reactor system.

taken off. If the flow rate of the feed is $f$ and the flow through the reactor is $q$,

$$f = qc. \tag{1}$$

The conversion $c$ is a function of $T$ the temperature of operation, $q$ the flow rate, and $s$ the total flow that has passed since the last regeneration of catalyst. A linear form of relationship is assumed, namely

$$c = c_1 T - c_2 q - c_3 s. \tag{2}$$

If the time of the process is divided into units of equal length, which for convenience will be called days, and a suffix $n$ denotes the number of the day after regeneration,

$$s_N = \sum_1^N q_n. \tag{3}$$

The term $c_3 s$ represents the decline of the conversion due to the deterioration of the catalyst.

The reaction is endothermic and requires the supply of a quantity of heat $Q$. If $T_0$ is temperature of the feed, $c_p$ the specific heat of the reactants and $\Delta H$ the heat of reaction,

$$Q = q c_p (T - T_0) + (\Delta H) f c. \tag{4}$$

The daily profit will be

$$P = v_1 f - v_2 Q - v_3 (1 - c) q - v_4. \tag{5}$$

The first term represents net increase of value of the product over the raw material, the second is the cost of heating, the third includes the cost of separation and return of the unreacted A, and the fourth the fixed charges.

If $P_n$, the profit on the $n$th day of operation after a catalyst replacement, is known from plant experience and if the cost of a

167

catalyst replacement is $R$, the average profit over a period of $N$ days of operation and $M$ days of replacement is

$$\left(\sum_1^N P_n - R\right)/(N + M). \qquad (6)$$

The optimal value of $N$ may now be found by calculating this expression for various $N$ until the maximum is reached.

This is a purely deterministic situation; another deterministic case which Roberts considers is the problem of actually determining the daily operating values of $T_n$ and $q_n$ that will maximize the total profit over a period of $N$ days. This can be formulated as a dynamic program by considering the state of the system to be given by $s$. If $f_N(s)$ is the maximum profit that can be made in $N$ days, starting in the state $s$, and if $g(s,T,q)$ is the daily profit starting the day in state $s$ and using conditions $T$ and $q$ [this is calculated from Eqs. (1)–(5)], then

$$f_N(s) = \underset{T,q}{\text{Max}} \{g(s,T,q) + f_{N-1}(s + q), -R + f_{N-1}(0)\}. \qquad (7)$$

The first quantity to be maximized is the profit of the day plus the maximum profit to be obtained in the remaining days by continuing to operate with the same catalyst. The second term is the cost of catalyst replacement plus maximum profit attainable starting with new catalyst, and we would choose the better alternative. An optimal operating policy is thus developed.

To return to our problem, however, we shall assume that $P_n$ is known, either from such an analysis or from plant experience, but that there is a stochastic element in the regeneration of the catalyst. The regeneration may produce a good catalyst which will remain good for the subsequent operating cycle or it may produce a poor catalyst that remains poor. Let the probability of getting a good catalyst be $p$ and that of getting a poor one $p' = 1 - p$. If $P_n$ and $P_n'$ are the daily profits from good and bad catalyst $n$ days old,

$$P_n > P_n' \quad \text{for all } n \qquad (8)$$

Now let

$f_N(t) =$ the expected profit from an $N$-stage process beginning with good catalyst $t$ days old

$g_N(t) =$ the expected profit from an $N$-stage process beginning with poor catalyst $t$ days old

Then at any stage we have the alternatives of continuing to operate or of shutting down and regenerating. If the latter alternative is taken, then the expected profit on restarting will be

$$pf_{N-1}(0) + p'g_{N-1}(0).$$

Thus, applying the principle of optimality,

$$f_N(t) = \text{Max} \{P_t + f_{N-1}(t+1), -R + pf_{N-1}(0) + p'g_{N-1}(0)\} \quad (9)$$

$$g_N(t) = \text{Max} \{P'_t + g_{N-1}(t+1), -R + pf_{N-1}(0) + p'g_{N-1}(0)\} \quad (10)$$

where

$$f_1(t) = P_t, \quad g_1(t) = P'_t, \quad p + p' = 1. \quad (11)$$

Here the functional equations have to be solved simultaneously.

We can generalize this immediately to a regeneration which might produce more than two qualities of catalyst. If the quality of catalyst can be characterized by a parameter $\gamma$, so that $P_n$ becomes $P_n(\gamma)$ and $f_N(t)$ becomes $f_N(t;\gamma)$, and if the regeneration produces a quality in the range $\gamma \pm \frac{1}{2}d\gamma$ with probability $p(\gamma)\,d\gamma$, then

$$f_N(t,\gamma)$$
$$= \text{Max} \left\{P_t(\gamma) + f_{N-1}(t+1,\gamma), -R + \int_0^\infty f_{N-1}(0,\gamma)p(\gamma)\,d\gamma\right\}.$$
$$(12)$$

Roberts has generalized the model in other directions by considering the constants $c_1$, $c_2$ and $c_3$ to be stochastic variables and has discussed what can be done in the way of optimal control when only probabilistic information about them is available (Roberts, 1960b).

# 9

# The Optimal Operation of Existing Reactors

---

*But the principal failing occurred in the sailing,*
*And the Bellman, perplexed and distressed,*
*Said he had hoped, at least, when the wind blew due East,*
*That the ship would not travel due West!*

---

As has been mentioned in Chapter 1 we shall not in this book attempt to go into the subject of chemical reactor control. We touch only the fringe of it here by paraphrasing certain design problems in the language of the control of operating conditions. If the data are available and the reactor is properly designed, the optimal policy for the operating variables will have been found in the process. However, many reactors are in service for which data have become available later, perhaps on the basis of the reactor operation itself (see, for example, Annable, 1952), and it is useful to see how this type of control can be used within the limitations of the existing design. Thus in a cold shot adiabatic reactor we cannot easily change the sizes of bed, but the bypass rates are immediately controllable. We shall usually assume that design data have become available to allow of an improvement in steady state operating conditions, although this new information may not be as complete as we would wish. An iterative use of this technique is a form of adaptive control (Rudd *et al.*, 1961), but the discussion of this lies outside our present scope, as does also nonsteady state control (except in the case of a batch reactor, the behavior of which in time is entirely analogous to the steady-state behavior of the tubular reactor in space).

## 9.1. The Stirred Tank Reactor Sequence

When a stirred tank sequence is designed *ab initio*, the holding time of each stage and its operating temperature are calculated. If it is already built the volume of each stage is fixed. This fixes the ratio of holding times and allows only the choice of flow rate and temperature. For a single reaction with a stoichiometric objective function we know that the optimal temperature policy is disjoint. This leads to a very simple method of control of a sequence of $R$ reactors, which applies even though the kinetics of the reaction are quite unknown. Since

$$q(c_r - c_{r+1}) = V_r r(c_r, T_r)$$

and the $V_r$ are fixed, each term of the series

$$\sum_1^R (c_r - c_{r+1}) = c_1 - c_{R+1}$$

must be maximized individually. Thus if measurements of $c$ can be made between stages, $T_R$ is first adjusted so that $(c_R - c_{R+1})$ is maximized, then $T_{R-1}$ so that $(c_{R-1} - c_R)$ is maximized, and so on down the line. The disjointness assures us that this will give the optimal operation of the whole reactor. Indeed this is a fully adaptive process, for a correlation between the fluctuations of $(c_r - c_{r+1})$ and $T_r$ will give an estimate of $\partial r/\partial T$, and $T_r$ can then be adjusted to bring this to zero. Any bounds on the temperature must of course be observed, but this is no problem.

In the case of simultaneous reactions, operating experience may lead to an estimate of the transformation of state

$$c_r^k = \mathfrak{I}_r^k(c_{r+1}^1, \ldots c_{r+1}^m; T_r)$$

that the reactor effects. Usually such an estimation will have only a limited range of validity but, as we have seen, this in no way hinders a dynamic programming optimization. When the improved state has been reached, new estimates of $\mathfrak{I}_r^k$ may be sought and used for further improvement.

If the kinetics of the reactions are known the methods of Section 5.7 can be applied with $V_r$ fixed.

172

## 9.2. *The Multibed Adiabatic Reactor*

### (1) *Interchanger Cooling*

In this case we may suppose that the bed volumes are fixed but that some latitude remains in the choice of temperature. Since nothing can be done about the cost of the beds we may take as the objective function [cf. Eq. (6.1.8)]

$$\sum_1^R p_r = \sum_1^R \{(c'_r - c_r) - \mu |T'_{r+1} - T_r|\}. \tag{1}$$

Then

$$c'_{r+1} = c_r \tag{2}$$

and the quantities

$$\theta_r = \int_{c_r}^{c'_r} \frac{dc}{r_r(c)} \tag{3}$$

are fixed. Let

$$f_R(c'_{R+1}, T'_{R+1}) = \text{Max} \sum_1^R p_r. \tag{4}$$

Then, by the principle of optimality,

$$f_R(c'_{R+1}, T'_{R+1}) = \text{Max} \{p_R + f_{R-1}(c'_R, T'_R)\}. \tag{5}$$

With existing interchangers there will probably be some restrictions on the relation between $T'_{r+1}$ and $T_r$. These may be put in the form

$$|T_r - T'_{r+1}| = \phi_r(T'_{r+1}). \tag{6}$$

The recursive equations (5) can now be solved by making use of (1), (2), (3), and (6). The simplest method is by direct calculation. Given $T'_{R+1}$ and $c'_{R+1}$, any trial value for $T_R$ may be taken and the integral (3) with variable upper limit computed until the value $\theta_R$ is reached. This then fixes $c'_R$ and enables the calculation of the right-hand side of (5). Successive trials of $T_R$ within the permitted range will achieve the maximum. The analytical relationships are no longer as simple as before and no easy presentation along the lines of Section 6.1 is possible. However, the method is quite straightforward and produces the optimal operating policy. It can be extended to simultaneous reactions but is subject to the usual difficulties of dimensionality.

173

## (2) *Cold Shot Cooling*

If we put $\theta_r = V_r/q$, where $q$ is the rate of flow through the last bed, then the $\theta_r$ will be fixed and (6.4.6) gives

$$\theta_r = \lambda_r \int_{c_r}^{c'_r} \frac{dc}{r_r(c)}. \tag{7}$$

In the notation of Section 6.4

$$c_r = \mu_{r+1}c'_{r+1}, \quad t_r = \mu_{r+1}t'_{r+1} \tag{8}$$

and since the $V_r$ are fixed we may take as profit function

$$P_R = \sum_1^R \lambda_r(c'_r - c_r). \tag{9}$$

In this case the simple graphical construction may be retained; for if

$$f_R(c'_{R+1};t'_{R+1}) = \text{Max } P_R \tag{10}$$

the principle of optimality gives

$$f_R(c'_{R+1},t'_{R+1}) = \text{Max } [\lambda_R(c'_R - c_R) + f_{R-1}(c'_R,t'_R)]. \tag{11}$$

Then, picking any point $c_R,t_R$ on the ray through $c'_{R+1},t'_{R+1}$, we can integrate along an adiabatic until (7) is satisfied and so calculate the expression on the right-hand side of (11). The point $(c_R,t_R)$ which gives the maximum is the same for all conditions $(c'_{R+1},t'_{R+1})$ that lie on this ray. By varying the slope of the ray the loci $\Gamma_R$ and $\Gamma'_R$ are generated just as before.

Such a diagram would be extremely useful if the preheater were subject to uncontrollable variations, as it might be if it were an interchanger dependent on another part of the plant. In this case the sequence of curves $\Gamma'_1, \Gamma_1, \Gamma'_2, \ldots, \Gamma_{R-1}$ could be drawn and the curve $\Gamma'_R$ on which exit conditions from bed $R$ should lie. This last is the curve $(c'_R,t'_R)$ for which

$$\theta_R = \lambda_R \int_0^{c'_R} \frac{dc}{r_R(c)} \tag{12}$$

and

$$r_R(c) = r(c, c + t_R). \tag{13}$$

With this set of curves we need only keep watch on the inlet temperature $t_R$ in order to calculate immediately the optimal bypass rates. We do this by drawing a line of unit slope from $(0,t_R)$ to $\Gamma'_R$, a ray to $\Gamma_{R-1}$, another line of unit slope to $\Gamma'_{R-1}$, and so on up to $\Gamma'_1$.

174

The values of $\mu_r$ can then be taken from the ratios of the distances from the origin to the points $(c_{r-1},t_{r-1})$ and $(c'_r,t'_r)$ and the control made accordingly. This is shown for $R = 3$ in Fig. 9.1.

The same calculation could be put on a computer which might

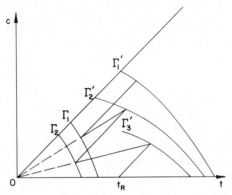

FIG. 9.1. Optimal cold shot control calculation.

even be organized to adjust the bypass rates. A similar calculation could be performed, but with greater difficulty, for $m$ simultaneous reactions.

## *9.3. Control with a Decaying Catalyst*

The performance of a catalyst will often deteriorate as the catalyst becomes coated with carbon or poisoned with impurities from the process stream. This may be reflected by introducing a parameter $\tau$ into the kinetic expression, $r(c,T;\tau)$. This parameter might be the time elapsed since the installation of the catalyst or the total volume of reactants passed since its regeneration. The question is considered by Hougen and Watson (1947), who give expressions for the dependence of $r$ on $\tau$. The particular form does not concern us here; we assume that a satisfactory expression has been developed. We want to know how the control of an adiabatic reactor should depend on $\tau$.

If the expression $r(c,T;\tau)$ is sufficiently well founded that a strict interpretation may be put upon $\tau$, the matter is straightforward enough. A machine computation along the lines of the preceding section can be performed for various values of $\tau$ and the optimal policy tabulated as a function of $\tau$. Operating instructions would

175

then detail the changes to be made at various times. However, the expression $r(c,T;\tau)$ may describe the course of the decay well enough, but it may not be possible to estimate the value of $\tau$ at any particular time except from the current behavior of the reactor. This would be the case if unpredictable variations of catalyst quality could be represented by suitably chosen initial values of $\tau$ and the subsequent decay followed a sequence of values of $\tau$ not necessarily very uniform. Two cases arise, the first in which all beds can be represented by the same value of $\tau$, the second in which they cannot. In the first case all that is required is that $T_R'$ should be calculated as a function of $T_R$ for various $\tau$. Then a measurement of these two temperatures will allow estimation of the current value of $\tau$. In the second case an estimate of $\tau$ must be made for each bed and this requires measurement of inlet and exit temperatures for each bed as well as the inlet (or exit) composition. Tables may be prepared showing $T_r'$ as functions of $T_r$ and $c_r$ for various $\tau$ and from these an estimate of $\tau$ is made for each bed. This estimate is then transmitted to the computer which does an optimal control calculation with

$$r_r(c) = r[c,T_r + H(c - c_r);\tau_r]$$

as the reaction rate in bed $r$.

## 9.4. The Optimal Control of a Batch Reactor

If $t$ is the time from the end of the batch process, the course of a single reaction is described by the equations (cf. Section 3.6)

$$\frac{dc}{dt} = -r(cT) \tag{1}$$

$$\frac{dT}{dt} = -Hr(c,T) + Q. \tag{2}$$

$Q$ is proportional to the rate of heat removal. We shall consider the problem of so controlling the reaction that a given conversion is achieved in the shortest possible time.

If it is possible to control the temperature exactly as we would wish, we know from Chapter 7 that we should always choose it so as to maximize the reaction rate. Let $c_1 = c(0)$ be the fixed conversion that we want to obtain; then if the initial state is $c_0$ the time to reach $c_1$ is given by

176

$$\theta = \int_{c_0}^{c_1} \frac{dc}{r(c,T)}. \tag{3}$$

If

$$f(c_0) = \text{Min } \theta \tag{4}$$

the principle of optimality gives the differential equation

$$-f'(c_0) = \text{Min } \frac{1}{r(c,T)} = \frac{1}{R(c)}, \tag{5}$$

as in Section 7.1. $R(c)$ is the maximum value of $r(c,T)$, which is attained when $T = T_m(c)$. If $T$ is restricted to lie in the interval $(T_*, T^*)$, then $R(c)$ is modified by holding $T$ at one of these bounds when $T_m$ goes outside of them. This optimal path is shown in Fig. 9.2

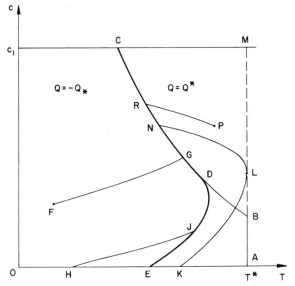

FIG. 9.2. Optimal control for a batch reaction.

as a curve ABC in the $c,T$ plane. The value of $Q$ required to keep the reactor on this path is given by Eq. (2):

$$Q = Hr(c,T) + \frac{dT}{dt}$$

$$= \{H - T'_m(c)\}R(c). \tag{6}$$

However, it is not possible to control the temperature directly; in reality it is $Q$ that is immediately accessible. If the initial temperature is $T_0$ and $(c_0, T_0)$ does not lie on the path ABC, or if it does

177

lie on this path but Eq. (6) demands an unattainable value of $Q$, then this optimal path cannot be followed for the whole course of the reaction. What then is the optimal form of control?

To answer this question we must look at both Eqs. (1) and (2) and apply our direct control to $Q$. We will assume that the controller is a cooler-heater that can work between certain limits

$$-Q_* \leq Q \leq Q^*. \tag{7}$$

If the controller is incapable of heating, at least it can be shut off so that $Q_*$ may be equal to zero. Let

$g(c_0, T_0)$ = the minimum time required to reach $c = c_1$
from the initial state $c_0, T_0$.

Then if a move is made to $c_0 + \delta c_0, T_0 + \delta T_0$ this will take a time

$$\int_{c_0}^{c_0 + \delta c_0} \frac{dc}{r(c, T)}$$

and the subsequent path will take at least $g(c_0 + \delta c_0, T_0 + \delta T_0)$. Hence by the principle of optimality

$$g(c_0, T_0) = \text{Min} \left[ \int_{c_0}^{c_0 + \delta c_0} \frac{dc}{r(c, T)} + g(c_0 + \delta c_0, T_0 + \delta T_0) \right]. \tag{8}$$

This minimum has to be attained by rightly choosing the value of $Q$ during the interval in which $c$ increases from $c_0$ to $c_0 + \delta c_0$. Since

$$\frac{\delta T_0}{\delta c_0} \doteq H - \frac{Q}{r(c_0, T_0)}$$

we have in the limit as $\delta c_0 \rightarrow 0$,

$$0 = \text{Min} \left[ \frac{1}{r(c_0, T_0)} + g_c + g_T \left\{ H - \frac{Q}{r(c_0, T_0)} \right\} \right]$$

where $g_c = \partial g / \partial c_0$, $g_T = \partial g / \partial T_0$. Since $r(c_0, T_0)$ is always positive we can multiply throughout by it to give

$$\text{Min} \left[ 1 + g_c r(c_0, T_0) + g_T \{ H r(c_0, T_0) - Q \} \right] = 0. \tag{9}$$

The optimal policy for $Q$ is now evident, for if $g_T > 0$, $Q$ should be made as large as possible whereas if $g_T < 0$, $Q$ should have its least value. This is common sense for it means that if the minimum time increases with increasing temperature the reactor should be cooled as much as possible, whereas if it decreases with increasing temperature heating (or at least no cooling) is called for. It is a form of

178

control variously known as relay, on-off, or bang-bang, and has been much studied in connection with linear systems. The main problem is to determine the switching boundary across which $Q$ jumps from its least to its greatest value. This is clearly the locus along which $g_T = 0$. Intuitively we would say that this will be the curve ABC which solves the previous problem, for on this curve $g$ would seem to be a minimum with respect to variations in $T$, and so $g_T = 0$. Also, we observe that if $g_T = 0$ Eq. (9) reduces to Eq. (5).

To prove this let us consider the characteristic equations of the partial differential equation (9). They are

$$\frac{dc_0}{ds} = r(c_0, T_0) \tag{10}$$

$$\frac{dT_0}{ds} = Hr(c_0, T_0) - Q \tag{11}$$

$$\frac{dg}{ds} = -1 \tag{12}$$

$$\frac{dg_c}{ds} = -g_c \frac{\partial r}{\partial c} - g_T H \frac{\partial r}{\partial c} \tag{13}$$

$$\frac{dg_T}{ds} = -g_c \frac{\partial r}{\partial T} - g_T H \frac{\partial r}{\partial T}. \tag{14}$$

Equations (10) and (11) can be divided by (12) to give the basic Eqs. (1) and (2). From Eq. (14) we see that if the locus $\partial r / \partial T = 0$ is a characteristic then it is one of constant $g_T$. But we have seen that it can be made to satisfy the first three equations and that at the point C $g_T$ certainly vanishes, for $g = 0$ on $c = c_1$ and so $g_T = 0$ along this line. It follows that $g_T$ vanishes along BC and that this is the switching boundary.

The optimal control policy is very simple. If the state of the reactor lies to the left of BC the heater should be used until the state reaches the boundary, after which $Q$ should be controlled by Eq. (6) until the desired conversion is reached. If the state of the reactor is to the right of the boundary, maximum cooling is applied until the boundary is reached and followed. It only remains to consider what happens if the value of $Q$ required by Eq. (6) exceeds the maximum $Q^*$. Let D be the point on BC where Eq. (6) first gives the value $Q^*$. Then clearly there is no difficulty with paths such as FGC or PRC which first meet BC above D. If the curve DE is the

179

solution of Eqs. (1) and (2) with $Q = Q^*$ we should take as switching boundary the curve CDE. Then such an initial condition as H calls for $Q = -Q_*$ and leads to a path HJDC, for this path meets DE at J and will be held on the path JD by switching to $Q = Q^*$ at J. After D it can be held on the path DC, by varying $Q$ according to (6). The optimal policy as a function of time is shown for the various paths in Fig. 9.3.

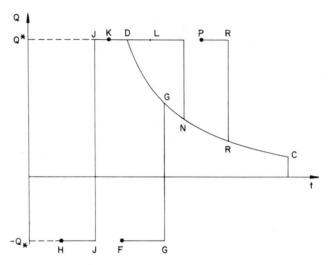

Fig. 9.3. Optimal control policy as a function of time. (The curves are drawn to terminate at the same point of the time axis, and the beginnings of paths are marked with a dot.)

The limitation $T \leq T^*$ leads to a limitation of the region of permissible initial states. If KLN (Fig. 9.2) is the trajectory with $Q = Q^*$ which is just tangent to the vertical line $T = T^*$, then any path issuing from the triangular region KAL will certainly achieve a temperature greater than $T^*$. Thus if M is the point $(c_1, T^*)$, the region of permitted initial states is bounded on the right by the curve KLM.

## 9.5. Further Problems in Batch Reactor Control

A wide variety of problems of the type just considered are amenable to dynamic programming and may be interpreted for both batch and tubular reactors. The generalization of the preceding example to simultaneous reactions is quite straightforward. The switching boundary becomes a surface which is the solution of the problem with full control of temperature; such problems have been fully discussed in Chapter 7. Another way of controlling the reaction in a batch reactor would be to add one or more of the reactants slowly. This would seem to be a rather economical way of doing the job since the addition of reactant will both control the reaction rate and absorb heat. We will sketch a simple case of this form of control; a similar case has been mentioned by Katz (1960b).

The reaction is $\sum_1^n \alpha_i A_i = 0$ and the total time it goes on is $\theta$, a period fixed by the cycle of operation. Let

$N_i(t)$ = number of moles of $A_i$ present at time $t$ after the start of the reaction,

$N_{i0}$ = $N_i(0)$,

$n_i(t)$ = rate of addition of $A_i$ (moles/unit time),

$N(t)$ = extent of reaction (moles).

Then

$$N_i(t) = N_{i0} + \int_0^t n_i(t) \, dt + \alpha_i N(t) \tag{1}$$

or

$$dN_i/dt = n_i + \alpha_i R(N_1, \ldots N_n, T), \tag{2}$$

where $R = dN/dt$ is the gross rate of reaction (moles/unit time) expressed in terms of the number of moles present and the temperature $T$.

To form a heat balance, let

$-\Delta H$ = heat evolved for unit increase of $N$,

$c_{pi}$ = specific heat of $A_i$,

$Q(t)$ = rate of heat removal,

$T_f$ = temperature of cold reactants as they are added.

Then

$$(\sum c_{pi} N_i) \frac{dT}{dt} = (-\Delta H) R(N_j, T) - \sum_1^n n_i(t) c_{pi}(T - T_f) - Q(t). \tag{3}$$

The functions $n_i(t)$ and $Q(t)$, $0 \leq t \leq \theta$, have to be chosen to maximize some objective function. We will take this to be a simple material profit function minus a cost proportional to the amount of heat removed. If $v_i$ is the value of a mole of $A_i$, the gain in value will be $(\sum \alpha_i v_i) N(\theta)$ since only reaction contributes to a gain in value. The total heat removed is $\int_0^\theta Q(t)\, dt$ and if we ascribe to it a unit cost of $\lambda(\sum \alpha_i v_i)$ we may consider the objective function

$$\int_0^\theta \{R(N_j, T) - \lambda Q(t)\}\, dt. \tag{4}$$

Let

$$f(N_{i0}, T_0, \theta) = \text{Max} \int_0^\theta \{R - \lambda Q\}\, dt \tag{5}$$

when $N_i$ and $T$ are governed by Eqs. (2) and (3),

$$N_i(0) = N_{i0}, \qquad T(0) = T_0 \tag{6}$$

and $n_i(t)$, $Q(t)$ are chosen optimally. Dividing the interval $(0, \theta)$ into $(0, \tau)$ and $(\tau, \theta)$, we have by the principle of optimality

$$f(N_{i0}, T_0, \theta) = \text{Max} \left[ \int_0^\tau \{R - \lambda Q\}\, dt + f[N_i(\tau), T(\tau), \theta - \tau] \right]. \tag{7}$$

Letting $\tau \to 0$ and expanding the functions we arrive at the partial differential equation

$$f_\theta = \text{Max} \left[ \begin{array}{l} R_0 - \lambda Q_0 + \sum_1^n f_{N_i} \{n_{i0} + \alpha_i R_0\} \\[2mm] + f_T \{(-\Delta H) R_0 - \sum_1^n n_{i0} c_{pi} (T_0 - T_f) - Q_0\} / (\sum c_{pi} N_{i0}) \end{array} \right] \tag{8}$$

where $f_{N_i} = \partial f / \partial N_{i0}$, $f_T = \partial f / \partial T_0$, $R_0 = R(N_{i0}, T_0)$ and $n_{i0}$ and $Q_0$ are the choices to be made of the control variables. This can be rearranged to give

$$f_\theta = \text{Max} \left[ \begin{array}{l} R_0 \{1 + \sum \alpha_i f_{N_i} + (-\Delta H) f_T / (\sum c_{pi} N_{i0})\} \\[2mm] + \sum n_{i0} \{f_{N_i} - f_T c_{pi} (T_0 - T_f) / (\sum c_{pi} N_{i0})\} \\[2mm] - Q_0 \{\lambda + f_T / (\sum c_{pi} N_{i0})\} \end{array} \right] \tag{9}$$

$$= \text{Max}\ A + \sum n_{i0} B_i - Q_0 C.$$

Again a bang-bang control is indicated. If

$$0 \le n_{i0} \le f_i, \qquad -Q_* \le Q_0 \le Q^*, \tag{10}$$

then the optimal policy is

$$n_{i0} = f_i, \qquad B_i > 0; \qquad n_{i0} = 0, \qquad B_i < 0;$$
$$Q_0 = -Q_*, \qquad C > 0; \qquad Q_0 = Q^*, \qquad c < 0. \tag{11}$$

The switching surfaces are those on which $B_i = 0$ and $C = 0$.

182

## 9.5. FURTHER PROBLEMS IN BATCH REACTOR CONTROL

In this generality the problem is clearly cursed with dimensionality and it is unlikely that one would wish to add all the reactants simultaneously. If only one reactant, say $A_1$, is added and the rest are all present at the start, the number of variables can be reduced from $n + 2$ to four. Since $n_i = 0$, $i = 2, \ldots n$, $dN_i = \alpha_i dN$ for these $i$ and we can replace all the variables $N_1, \ldots N_n$ in $f$ by two, namely $N_1$ and $N$. Then all terms except $i = 1$ drop out from the second line of (9), and

$$\sum \alpha_i f_{N_i} = f_N.$$

We have only scratched the surface of the corpus of control problems that might be posed in the context of chemical reactors. It is evident that dynamic programming is a valuable tool in such studies, but even more powerful ones are currently being forged and will doubtless soon be applied to these problems. On the intelligent and perceptive use of these tools will depend the practical progress of chemical engineering cybernetics during the next few years.

## References

Amundson, N. R. 1955. Three problems in chemical reactor design. *Ingenieur (Utrecht)* **67** No. 37, 1–6.

Amundson, N. R. 1958. Class notes on reactor design. Unpublished material.

Amundson, N. R., and Aris, R. 1957. Note on longitudinal diffusion or mixing in beds. *A.I.Ch.E. Journal* **3**, 280–282.

Amundson, N. R., and Bilous, O. 1956. Optimum temperature gradients in tubular reactors. I. General theory and methods. II. Numerical study. *Chem. Eng. Sci.* **5**, 81–92 and 115–126.

Amundson, N. R., Coste, J., and Rudd, D. F. 1961. Taylor diffusion in tubular reactors. Can. J. Chem. Eng. in press.

Annable, D. 1952. Application of the Temkin kinetic equation to ammonia synthesis in large-scale reactors. *Chem. Eng. Sci.* **1**, 145–154.

Aris, R. 1960a. On Denbigh's optimum temperature sequence. *Chem. Eng. Sci.* **12**, 56–64.

Aris, R. 1960b. The optimal design of stagewise adiabatic reactors. Conference on Optimization Techniques in Chemical Engineering, New York University, May 18, 1960. 125–160.

Aris, R. 1960c. The determination of optimal operating conditions by the methods of dynamic programming. Diskussionstagung der Bunsengesellschaft, October 20–21, 1960. (To appear in Z. Elektrochem. **65**, 229–244, 1961.)

Aris, R. 1960d. Studies in optimization I: The optimum design of adiabatic reactors with several beds. *Chem. Eng. Sci.* **12**, 243–252.

Aris, R. 1960e. Studies in optimization II: Optimum temperature gradients in tubular reactors. *Chem. Eng. Sci.* **13**, 18–29.

Aris, R. 1960f. Studies in optimization III: The optimum conditions in sequences of stirred tank reactors. *Chem. Eng. Sci.*, **13**, 75–81.

Aris, R. 1961. Studies in optimization IV: The optimum conditions for a single reaction. *Chem. Eng. Sci.*, in press.

Aris, R., Rudd, D. F., and Amundson, N. R. 1960. On optimum cross-current extraction. *Chem. Eng. Sci.* **12**, 88–97.

Bellman, R. 1956. Dynamic programming and Lagrange multipliers. *Proc. Natl. Acad. Sci. U. S.* **42**, 767–769.

Bellman, R. 1957. "Dynamic Programming." Princeton Univ. Press, Princeton, New Jersey.

Bellman, R. 1958a. Dynamic programming and its application to variational problems in mathematical economics. *Proc. Symposia Appl. Math. Am. Math. Soc.* **8**, 115–138.

Bellman, R. 1958b. Some new techniques in the dynamic programming solution of variational problems. *Quart. Appl. Math.* **16**, 295–305.

Bellman, R. 1961. "Adaptive Control Processes: A Guided Tour." Princeton Univ. Press, Princeton, New Jersey.

Bellman, R., Kalaba, R., and Aris, R. 1960. Some optimum problems in chemical engineering. Chem. Eng. Prog. Symposium Series, **56**, 95–102.

Bilous, O., and Piret, E. L. 1955. Continuous stirred tank reactors: A new graphical method for complex reactions and reflux designs. *A.I.Ch.E. Journal* **1**, 480–487.

185

REFERENCES

Calderbank, P. H. 1953. Contact-process converter design. *Chem. Eng. Progr.* **49**, 585–590.

Coste, J. 1959. Chemical tubular reactor studies. Sensitivity and diffusion. Ph.D. Thesis. Department of Chemical Engineering, University of Minnesota, Minneapolis, Minnesota.

Danckwerts, P. V. 1958. The effect of incomplete mixing on homogeneous reactions. *Chem. Eng. Sci.* **8**, 93–102.

Denbigh, K. G. 1944. Velocity and yield in continuous reaction systems. *Trans. Faraday Soc.* **40**, 352–373.

Denbigh, K. G. 1947. Continuous reactions. Part II. The kinetics of steady state polymerisation. *Trans. Faraday Soc.* **43**, 648–660.

Denbigh, K. G. 1951. The kinetics of continuous reaction processes. *J. Appl. Chem. (London)* **1**, 227–236.

Denbigh, K. G. 1958. Optimum temperature sequences in reactors. *Chem. Eng. Sci.* **8**, 125–131.

Denbigh, K. G. 1960. Instantaneous and overall reaction yields. *In* "Second European Symposium on Chemical Reaction Engineering." See *Chem. Eng. Sci.* **14**, 25–38 (1961).

Denbigh, K. G., Hicks, M., and Page, F. M. 1948. The kinetics of open reaction systems. *Trans. Faraday Soc.* **44**, 479–494.

Grütter, W. F., and Messikommer, B. H. 1960. Systematische Ausbeuteberechnung für isotherme Reaktoren im Falle zusammengesetzter Reaktionen. *In* "Second European Symposium on Chemical Reaction Engineering." See *Chem. Eng. Sci.* **14**, 231–240 (1961).

Happel, J. 1958. "Chemical Process Economics." Wiley, New York.

Horn, F. 1958a. Optimalprobleme bei kontinuierlichen chemischen Prozessen. Dissertation Techn. Hochschule, Wien.

Horn, F. 1958b. Remarks in discussion of Denbigh's paper. *Chem. Eng. Sci.* **8**, 131–132.

Horn, F. 1960. Optimale Temperatur—und Konzentrationsverläufe. *In* "Second European Symposium on Chemical Reaction Engineering." See *Chem. Eng. Sci.* **14**, 77–89 (1961).

Horn, F. 1961. Über das Problem der optimalen Rührkesselkaskade für chemische Reaktionen. *Chem. Engr. Sci.*, in press.

Horn, F., and Küchler, L. 1959. Probleme bei reaktionstechnischen Berechnungen. *Chem.-Ingr. Tech.* **31**, 1–11.

Horn, F., and Troltenier, U. 1960. Über den optimalen Temperaturverlauf im Reaktionsrohr. *Chem.-Ingr. Tech.* **32**, 382–393.

Hougen, O. and Watson, K. M. 1947. "Chemical Process Principles," Vol. III: Kinetics and Catalysis. Wiley, New York.

Kalaba, R. 1960. Some mathematical aspects of optimization problems in engineering. Conference on Optimization Techniques in Chemical Engineering, New York University, May 18, 1960.

Kalman, R. E., Lapidus, L., and Shapiro, E. 1959. The optimal control of chemical and petroleum processes. "Proceedings of the Joint Symposium on Instrumentation and Computation in Process Development and Plant Design," May 11–13, 1959. Institution of Chemical Engineers, London.

186

## REFERENCES

Katz, S. 1960a. Best control actions in batch or pipeline reactors. Conference on Optimization Techniques in Chemical Engineering, New York University, May 18, 1960, pp. 57–78.

Katz, S. 1960b. Best temperature profiles in plug flow reactors: Methods of the calculus of variations. *Annals N. Y. Acad. Sci.*, **84**, 441–478.

Leitenberger, W. 1939. Thermische Beziehungen und Verlagerung der Kontaktmasse bei Schwefelsäurekontaktkesseln. *Chem. Fabrik* **12**, 281–292.

Piret, E. L., and Trambouze, P. J. 1959. Continuous stirred tank reactors: Designs for maximum conversions of raw material to desired product. Homogeneous reactions. *A.I.Ch.E. Journal* **5**, 384–390.

Potter, S. 1951. Some Notes on Lifemanship, with a Summary of Recent Researches in Gamesmanship. Holt, New York.

Roberts, S. M. 1960a. Dynamic programming formulation of the catalyst replacement problem. *Chem. Eng. Progr. Symposium Series*, **56**, 103–110.

Roberts, S. M. 1960b. Stochastic models for the dynamic programming formulation of the catalyst replacement problem. Conference on Optimization Techniques in Chemical Engineering, New York University, May 18, 1960, 171–188.

Rudd, D. F. 1960. A study of iterative optimization and on the design of processes subject to random failures. Ph.D. Thesis. Department of Chemical Engineering, University of Minnesota, Minneapolis, Minnesota.

Rudd, D. F., Aris, R., and Amundson, N. R. 1961. A study of iterative optimization. *A.I.Ch.E. Journal*, **7**, in press.

Swinnerton-Dyer, H. P. F. 1957. On an extremal problem. *Proc. London Math. Soc.* III, **7**, 568–583.

Taylor, G. I. 1954. The dispersion of matter in turbulent flow through a pipe. *Proc. Roy. Soc.* **A223**, 446–468.

Westbrook, G. 1960. The simulation, stabilization and optimization of stirred tank reactors on the digital computer, M.S. Thesis. Department of Chemical Engineering, University of Minnesota, Minneapolis, Minnesota.

Westbrook, G. 1961. The occurrence, classification, and optimization of allocation decisions in the chemical industry. M.A. Thesis, Department of Economics, University of Minnesota, Minneapolis, Minnesota.

Westbrook, G. T., and Aris, R. 1961. A new approach to chemical reactor design. *Ind. Eng. Chem.* **53**, 181–186.

Zweitering, T. N. 1959. The degree of mixing in continuous flow systems, *Chem. Eng. Sci.* **11**, 1–15.

\* \* \*

The Proceedings of the Second European Symposium on Chemical Reaction Engineering were published as Volume 14 of the Journal Chemical Engineering Science while the present work was in press. It should be said that this symposium contains more that is germane to our subject than it has been possible to indicate here.

187

# Index*

* The reader will find the bibliographic listings for the authors cited in this index on pages 185 to 187.

190